SCHOLASTIC COLLECTIONS

Compiled by Pie Corbett

Tales, Myths & Legends

© 1993 Scholastic Ltd

456789 789012

Published by Scholastic Ltd,
Villiers House,
Clarendon Avenue,
Leamington Spa,
Warwickshire CV32 5PR

Compiler Pie Corbett
Editors Christine Lee
Series designer Joy White
Designer Micky Pledge
Cover and illustrations Robin Lawrie

Designed using Aldus Pagemaker
Artwork by David Harban Design, Warwick
Printed in Great Britain by Ebenezer Baylis, Worcester

British Library Cataloguing-in-Publication Data
A catalogue record for this book is
available from the British Library.

ISBN 0-590-53112-3

Contents

THE BRAVE AND THE FAITHFUL

RIDDLES AND RUSES

WISHES AND SURPRISES

GODS AND GODDESSES

INTRODUCTION

When I sat down to put this collection together, I looked through many anthologies. Often I found good stories buried in a fusty, heavy language that made it almost impossible for children to enjoy them. So I wrote to storytellers and teachers whom I knew and asked them to send me stories that they enjoyed telling and that children enjoyed listening to.

This, then, is our ragbag of tales from around the world. These are stories that will act as a source for those who wish to tell stories. Of course, you can read these aloud but half of the magic will be missing. Below are some notes on how to begin telling stories. Do give it a go — those who have done find it addictive.

At the back of the book are notes which include suggested age levels for the stories, although what suits each group of children, each situation and each teller will vary. Most of the stories suggested for the youngest age group will suit older children as well. However, those suggested for the oldest children would probably not be right for the younger ones.

Storytelling weaves a spell that binds us all into one world community. We enter that other world where anything is possible, to think, to feel and to grow together. Our stories help sustain and create our society. They help to shape and fashion who we are, and help us to know and feel what is right and what is wrong. Stories should cherish the human spirit and as such should be a central part of every child's upbringing.

Notes on storytelling

If you want to *tell* some of these stories rather than *read* them, here are some brief suggestions as to how to set about it. It will take some time, plenty of practice and perhaps some courage too! The first time you put down a book and rely on the story, and yourself, may seem daunting. However, what you will quickly find is the sense of growing excitement as you watch the children's faces mesmerised by the tale. You can read their feelings as you tell the tale — and, far from not being good at it, you will probably find that it is easier than you at first thought. For, of course, those who are used to being with children (parents, playgroup helpers, teachers, and so on) will find that they are very skilled at storytelling because they spend most of their time talking with children in a 'story' way. So, follow these guidelines and give it a go.
• Look through this collection and find a story that you like. It is important to choose a story that you want to tell.
• You don't have to memorise the story word for word — the skill is to learn the structure of the story. I find it helps to draw the sequence of events. A list of a few keywords like a flow chart can also help.
• Don't be afraid to adapt the story — add in bits that occur to you as you are telling it. Take parts out that seem unnecessary. Adapt and adopt. Begin to make it your own.
• Practise telling the story to yourself — in the bath, in the car, while out walking. Say it out aloud as if you had an audience. The more times you repeat this, the more fixed in your mind the story becomes.
• Be quite sure about both the opening and the ending. Floundering at the end of a story is rather like forgetting the punchline to a joke.
• Try telling the story to a friend. Have a practice run on a one-to-one basis. Keep retelling it until you can say it in your sleep.

When the big day arrives, make sure that you are seated with your back to a wall. If you get a window behind you the children may be distracted from the start! If you can, organise the children so that they sit in a circle or horseshoe shape. Bring them in close to you. This is important. Long lines that stretch too far to the side and back of a hall mean that the children on the edges may well not be drawn into the story. Make sure that you can see every child's eyes — it is vital that you hold them with your eyes as you speak in order to maintain their interest in the story.

As you begin the story, you will need a way of gently drawing them in. This needs to be thought about — if you can get the children to 'listen' and look at you then their attention may be ready. Some storytellers use an object, some use a musical instrument. You may want to start by asking a question ('Have you ever woken up feeling really hungry?... Well in this story there was a fox who woke up and he was STARVING! So...').

As you tell the story, keep your eyes on the children and they will watch you. Use your voice — don't rush the telling. You can leave pauses, slow down, speed up, raise or lower your voice. All this should fit the tale, but you will find that it may happen almost without you noticing it.

Be aware that, with younger children, asking rhetorical questions can lead to difficulties. Don't be surprised if 35 children give you an answer! Think on your feet and make their comment a part of the story ('Yes, Jessica the giant was bigger than your Dad and she walked up the mountain to her cave').

If a child looks too anxious you may wish to soften the story in some way. This can be done with the tone of the voice or by adding a soothing comment ('But there was nothing to fear'). However, if the stories are to work, do not hesitate to get rid of unpleasant foxes, etc. Part of the importance of these tales is that children can meet all sorts of fears safely. At the end of the tale it will not be good enough to have the wicked fox just run away. Young children will not be satisfied with anything less than the object of their fear being got rid of for good.

Once you have told your story, find another group to tell it to. Then find another story. You already know many stories from your own childhood. Practise and then get telling. I know you will love it and I know that the children will as well.

Children as storytellers

The final move is to encourage the children to become storytellers as well. They can follow the same sort of process as you have done. Initially, they will find it easier to work from one of your tellings. Then they can move on to working from photocopied sheets. This is the process I use:
• I tell a straightforward story to a group. I find 'Mister Fox and his Bag' a good one to start with as it has a clear structure.
• The children then have to draw the 'map' of what happens in the story. This helps them to go over the story and fix the sequence of events.
• I then ask them to jot down any key phrases they may need.
• The children sit facing each other in pairs and take it in turn to tell parts of the story, helping each other out where necessary. They will need to practise telling the story several times.
• I then put two pairs together. Each pair takes it in turn to tell the story, helping each other if need be.
• They should then be ready to tell the story as a pair to a child from another class.

The more practice tellings they have, the more fluent the telling will become. Using a tape recorder and listening to their telling will also help them to become more effective and fluent.

Pie Corbett

THE STORY OF 'HOW' AND 'WHY'

How music came to the world

Tezcatlipoca[1], God of Heaven, came to Earth to admire his creation. At first he gazed about him with pride: the Earth teemed with life and movement and glowed with all the colours of the rainbow. But as he stood in the centre of the world feasting his eyes, his heart gradually filled with sadness for his ears heard only silence. Then Tezcatlipoca cried with a mighty voice to each of the four quarters in turn:

Come, O Wind!
Come, O Wind!
Come, O Wind!
Come, O Wind!

Then the Wind, which was scattered over the Earth, rose high above the world, and, whipping up the waters of the ocean and the manes of the trees, flew to the feet of the God of Heaven. There he rested his black wings and laid aside his endless sorrow and awaited the commands of Tezcatlipoca.

Tezcatlipoca spoke again: 'Wind, the Earth mourns under a blanket of silence. Although we have light and colour and fruit, we have no music. We must give music to all of creation: to the awakening dawn, to the dreaming man, to the waiting mother, to the passing water and the flying bird. Life should be all music.

'Go then! Fly through the endless sadness of the skies to the High House of the Sun, where the father Sun is surrounded by makers of music who play their flutes and sing in choirs in the warmth of his light. Go, and bring back to Earth the finest musicians so that the heart of the world may be filled with their joy.'

1. Pronounced 'Tez-cat-lee-pock-a'

Then the Wind flew over the Earth that was covered in silence and up into the sky until he reached the heavenly roof of the world where all the melodies lived in a nest of light. The Sun's musicians wore four colours: white were those of the cradle songs; red those of the epics of love and of war; sky-blue the wandering minstrels and yellow the flute players whose flutes were made of gold that the Sun himself had milled from the mountain peaks of the world.

When the Sun saw the Wind approaching, he called to his musicians: 'Here comes the bothersome Wind of Earth. Stop your music! Cease your singing! When he calls, do not answer him, for whoever does so will have to follow him back down there into silence.'

From the foot of the stairways of light that led into the house of the Sun, the Wind shouted with his dark voice: 'Come, O musicians!'

But none replied.

The Wind raised his voice and cried louder: 'Musicians! Singers! The Supreme Lord of the World is calling you....'

But the musicians remained as silent colours. Then they joined hands and began to circle round the Sun. Faster and faster and faster they whirled, until their colours blurred into a blinding white halo and they created a hot wind that scorched the wings of the Wind of Earth and sent him fleeing back to earth where he approached Tezcatlipoca with a hangdog look.

Then Tezcatlipoca was filled with fury. 'Selfish Sun!' he cried, 'who will not share his joy with the rest of creation!'

From his belt he took his lightning lash and whipped flocks of clouds from the remotest places, so that black with his rage and torn by his lightning, they assembled to besiege the House of the Sun. The Wind opened his great black wings and flew across the world carrying his army before him, and as they advanced across the skies, bringing darkness and chaos with them, Tezcatlipoca opened his mouth and his bottomless throat let loose the thunder's roar. And in the battle beneath the World's roof, the Sun, like a red beast, drowned.

Driven by terror, the musicians and singers then ran for shelter into the open arms of the Wind. He ceased his howling and caught them gently so as not to harm their delicate melodies, and then set out on his downward journey, no longer raging, but quiet and contented and full of care and love.

Below, Earth raised its wide dark eyes to heaven, and its great face shone, and it smiled. The trees raised their arms, the Quetzal[2] birds their wings, the flowers raised their faces and the fruits raised their cheeks to greet the Wind with its burden of wanderers that were to awaken the voices of its people. When that cargo of joy landed on Earth, the Sun's musicians exclaimed at its beauty and they spread to the four quarters, filled with wonder at what they found. Then the Wind ceased his complaining and sang, caressing the valleys, the forests and seas.

Thus was music born on the bosom of the earth, and thus did all things learn to sing: the awakening dawn, the dreaming man, the waiting mother, the flowing water and the flying bird. All life has had music from that time on.

Pamela Marre

The power of the small

At the beginning of Creation, everything was water. It was without any form and empty and dark, so God said, 'Let there be light.' And there was light, and then God divided the light from the darkness and called the light 'Day' and the dark 'Night', and that was his first day's work.

Then God said, 'Let the waters divide into those which are above and those which are below.' And the waters divided and God called those which were above 'Heaven', and that was his second day's work.

Then God said, 'Let the waters under the heavens gather together into one place and let dry land appear.' And so it happened, and God called the dry land Earth and the waters that had gathered together he called Seas. God was pleased and said, 'Let grass grow on the earth, and plants and trees, all of which will make seeds so that they can increase themselves.' All this happened, and that was his third day's work.

But the waters were jealous of the land. 'We were the first of all Creation, and we are the most powerful,' they cried.

And so they began to rise, higher and higher until they threatened to flood the earth and cover all the land. Then God became angry. 'You are too proud of your strength and too boastful!' he cried. 'If you do not stop rising I will send the sands to stop you!'

When the waters saw how tiny the grains of sand were, they began to laugh and mock. 'Hah! How can such tiny grains stand up against us? Why, our smallest waves can sweep them away!' And the waters carried on rising.

Then God was furious and commanded the sands to come and stop the seas. When they heard his command, the grains of sand were very frightened, but among them were those who gave comfort to the others

2. Pronounced 'Coatal'

saying, 'Do not fear! For while it is true that we are tiny and each of us on our own is insignificant, and the wind can carry us to the ends of the earth, if we all remain united, then the waters will see what kind of power we have.'

When the little grains of sand heard these words of comfort they came flying from all the corners of the earth and lay down one on top of the other beside each other at the shores of the seas. They rose up in mounds, in hills and in mountains, and formed a huge barrier that the waters could not overcome. And when the waters saw how the great army of grains of sand stood united, they gave up and retreated. That is why the water could not cover the earth and the land remained.

Pamela Marre

Six suns (or how the cock got his comb)

Long, long ago, when the world was still young, there was not just one sun in the sky. There were six. Winters were warm and pleasant, but in summer it was often too hot to go out in the daytime.

One year there was no rain to cool the earth and no clouds came to hide the heat of the six suns. The sky blazed with light and the earth cracked and crumbled. No birds sang, no flowers bloomed and no leaves grew on the trees. People hid inside their houses and only came out at night for water. Eventually even the lakes and underground streams began to dry up and the people lost all hope.

One night Yang said suddenly, 'I know what I must do. I will shoot the suns.'

Now Yang had a massive bow and long arrows flighted with feathers from the Mandarin duck. He was the best archer in the world, but people laughed when they heard his plan. 'The suns are too far away,' they said. 'Your arrows will never reach them.'

But when Yang went outside the next evening, many people followed him to watch. Yang climbed the high rocks at the edge of the lake and fixed an arrow on to the string of his huge bow. Instead of lifting his bow high, Yang took careful aim at the reflection of one of the suns in the shallow water below.

THWANG! Yang's arrow sped over the water and plunged into one of the suns. It sank at once. THWANG! Another arrow hit the second sun right in the centre and it too disappeared. THWANG! THWANG! The light of two more suns went out. Now there were only two left and already the air was cooler. Yang placed another arrow in his bow. THWANG! It sped over the water and put out the light of another sun.

'Look,' cried the people. 'The last sun is so scared it is trying to hide.'

Indeed the last, frightened sun was plunging through the sky and, before Yang could fit another arrow, it had fled behind a mountain. Only a deep red glow could be seen behind jagged peaks and the lake water reflected crimson as if with the blood of dead suns.

The next day it was as though it were still night-time, because the sun was too afraid to come out. The next dark day was the same, and the next and the next. People could not see to do their jobs. They began to call out to the sun, 'Come out. We will not hurt you. Yang has put his arrows away.'

'Our voices are too feeble,' a woman said. 'We need a louder voice. The tiger will roar and the sun will hear.' So they fetched a tiger.

'GRRROOORR!' it roared.

The noise was so frightening, that the sun thought the people were still angry. It stayed hidden.

'A cow has a loud voice,' a man said. 'A cow will moo and the sun will hear.' So they fetched a cow.

'MOOAH-MOO-OO-OO,' it mooed.

The noise was less frightening than the tiger's roar, but the sun was still afraid. It stayed hidden.

'A cock has a loud voice,' a girl said. 'The cock will crow and the sun will hear.' So they fetched a cock.

'COCK-A-LOK-A-LOO,' it crowed.

Now the sun liked this sound and was so curious to see what was making it, that it looked up over the edge of the horizon. As soon as the people saw the sun they cheered happily and the sun knew it was safe to come out. Since that time the sun has never been afraid, for the cock always tells the sun that it is safe for it to rise. To say 'thank you', the sun gave the cock a splendid comb for the top of its head. To this day the cock's comb is shaped like jagged peaks and it is crimson as if stained with the blood of dead suns.

Barrie Wade

The story of the Sun, the Moon and the Sea

Did you know that a long time ago Sun and Moon used to live here on Earth and their best friend in all the world was Sea? They were always going to Sea's house to play games, sing songs, eat and tell jokes.

Well, one day Sun and Moon were looking very sad and when their friend, Sea, asked them what was wrong they said, 'You never come to our house.'

And the Sea said, 'It's because your house is not big enough – you know that I've so many friends; wherever I go; they all insist on coming too.'

'Is that all?' they both cried. 'We'll build a house – the biggest house you've ever seen for the best party in the world!'

So they arranged the day and time, then Sun and Moon went away and hammered, nailed, chiselled, cooked, baked, boiled and fried all of Sea's favourite foods – Seaweed Pie, Snail Soup, Squid Delight (sounds simply scrumptious, doesn't it?).

The day arrived, and Sun and Moon, their enormous house built, were very pleased with themselves. Sea swam up to the house and knocked at the door three times. Beaming brightly, Sun and Moon opened it and said, 'Come on in.'

But Sea, always the cautious one, said, 'Are you sure?' then whispered, 'As you can see, all my friends insisted on coming; nobody would stay behind.'

Now Sun and Moon were impatient for the party to begin and so they replied, 'Come on in, we've plenty of food and drinks; there's music and a barbecue in the back... there's room for everyone. Let the party begin!'

So in swam the Sea with all its friends.

Now this is where you come into the story.... Who or what lives in the Sea?

(The children should now be encouraged to call out the names of different creatures or objects in the sea. However, tell them that they must pretend to be whatever they call out, such as Whale, Rock or Dolphin.)

Yes, you're right. There was the Dolphin, jumping and prancing... all the fishes, Cod, Salmon, Plaice, Trout, Goldfish... the Electric Eel (don't get too close!)... the Jellyfish, all wobbly and jolly... the Blue Whale, spluttering and bumping... all the Rocks, Pebbles, Coral and the wriggling Seaweed... the tickly Octopus; with all of its seven oops – eight legs!

It went on and on and on....

(The naming continues.)

The fierce White Shark always with the full orchestra playing the theme from *Jaws*... the Fishermen and their Boats... the Sea Monsters – all big and small... all the Shipwrecks and their Treasures.

Hold on, wait... what do you think was happening to Sun and Moon's house as all these creatures and objects, big and small, swam in?

Well you guessed it – the house was beginning to get extremely wet... it was crumbling, breaking... falling down!

Sun and Moon became worried and Sea looked at their faces and said,

'I'll stop if you want.'

'No,' said Sun and Moon. 'There is *still* room for everyone.'

So Sea and its friends kept on coming in.

Now Sun and Moon, who did not like getting their feet wet, decided to go upstairs; but the Sea and its friends followed them – *rising higher and higher.*

So Sun and Moon climbed out of the window on to the roof; but the Sea *kept on rising.*

So they climbed on to a tree, but the sea *still* kept on rising.

From the tree, they climbed on to a hill, but the Sea *kept on rising.*

So from the hill they climbed on to a larger hill; but the Sea was *still rising.*

Everyone was having such a good time – except Sun and Moon. They were so worried, they scrambled up to a mountain top... but you know what happened... yes the Sea was *still rising!*

They clung to each other and suddenly spied a small hole... where do you think?

Yes that's right – up in the SKY!

Quickly they climbed up and plugged the hole tightly to keep Sea out.

And do you know what – that is where the Sea's friends have remained to this very day.

Now Sun and Moon have to take it in turns to sleep; that is why we have Day and Night; for one of them has to keep an eye on Sea who after all this time is still rising and rising!

So I hope you all can swim... but don't worry if you can't; just get into a boat and row very, very quickly!

Sandra A. Agard

Tortoise and the party in the sky

Tortoise woke up one morning and gave a big yawn, followed by an enormous stretch. Then he heard a strange rumbling – RUMBLE... RUMBLE... RUMBLE.

He realised that the rumbling was coming from his stomach and that he was hungry. So he got out of bed and went to the kitchen; opened his cupboard, but it was empty – there was nothing there; not even a bone to lick. Poor Tortoise had not eaten for many days; he could find no food. Not even a single lettuce leaf. He had no money to buy any food, either.

RUMBLE... RUMBLE... RUMBLE continued his stomach.

Tortoise was so sad, and he went and sat down on the porch, wondering what to do.

Just then he heard a twittering and a flapping up in the sky.

When he looked up he saw all the Birds of the sky flying up and down. They were holding large baskets in their beaks and claws.

Tortoise was puzzled and tried to get their attention; but they were much too busy and ignored his cries. That is until Robin hopped down and Tortoise asked, 'What's going on?'

'Don't you know that the Birds are having a party in the sky?' replied Robin.

'Hmm,' thought Tortoise. 'A party means dancing, singing and, best of all, EATING!'

'Can I come too?' asked Tortoise.

'I don't see why not,' said Robin. 'I'll just ask the other Birds.'

And away he flew, soon to be back with the news that Tortoise *could* come to the party.

Now there was one difficulty. What can Birds do that Tortoises can not? That's right – FLY! How was Tortoise going to get to the party in the sky? One by one the Birds put forward their ideas.

Eagle tried to carry Tortoise in her strong claws; but they were much too sharp and scratched him.

Next several of the smaller birds tried carrying him; but he was much too heavy for them.

They tried building a ladder with as many boxes as they could find; and just managed to reach the tip of the sky. So Tortoise climbed and climbed and climbed; but was too scared to jump the gap between the boxes and the clouds. So he came all the way down again.

Then they got some balloons and tied them to a basket and asked the Wind to blow softly to take Tortoise to the sky. Wind did so, and all was going well until a swarm of bees came along.

BUZZ... BUZZ... BUZZ.

They looked neither left nor right, but went straight through the balloons.

POP... POP... POP.

Wind managed to catch the basket and put it down on the ground. Tortoise was a little shaken, but was still determined to get to the party.

Hawk, like Eagle, tried to carry Tortoise; but it was so ticklish and Tortoise wriggled so much that it proved impossible.

Dove suggested bringing the party to earth, but none of the Birds agreed. After all, it had simply taken ages to get all the food up to the sky.

Sparrow thought about booking a seat on an aeroplane, but there were no seats available (something about an Animals' Convention; but that's another story!).

Can you think of any other ways Tortoise could get to the party in the Sky?

Well, by now the Birds were getting a bit fed up. They were just about to leave Tortoise, when Owl, who had stayed up especially for the Party, said, 'Well, what do Birds have that Tortoises do not?'

Can you guess what it is? That's right – WINGS!

Each of the Birds unplucked a feather and stuck it on Tortoise and very soon Tortoise had a fine pair of wings.

After a few attempts (for it is very hard to fly straight away) Tortoise was soaring in the Sky with the Birds. It was brilliant... why had HE not been given wings? Higher and higher and higher he went until he reached the sky. Once there, he saw the delicious food and quite forgot his manners. He began to push, shove and fight the Birds for ALL the food. None of the Birds were getting anything. When they tried to stop him, he would just fly away. For what had the Birds given him... WINGS!

The Birds, by now very angry, called Robin and said, 'You told us to invite this greedy Tortoise to our party; get rid of him or we'll get rid of YOU!'

Now Robin liked being a member of the Bird family, so he had to think of something quickly. He thought and thought and thought. Suddenly he had an idea.

He flew down to Earth, got a large net and, as Tortoise was eating his fifth bowl of chocolate ice cream, the Birds quietly flew up to him and flung the net over him. Then they grabbed all the feathers that made up his wings and they all flew away, leaving Tortoise behind.

Without any wings, what happened to Tortoise? Yes, that's right. He began falling and falling and falling from the sky. As he fell, he called down to his friends, Hare and Rabbit, 'Hurry, run into my house, fetch all the mattresses and cushions. I'm coming DOWN!'

Hare and Rabbit ran into his house and pulled out all the mattresses and cushions and spread them over the stony ground. They watched as Tortoise fell and fell and FELL!

Tortoise landed on the mattresses and cushions so hard that he did a double-double-treble-treble somersault, bounced out and landed on the stony ground – so breaking his shell! Hare and Rabbit were horrified. They ran back into the house, found some glue and began to gather up all the pieces.

They tried as best as they could to stick all the pieces back together again. But it was like an enormous jigsaw puzzle, with many of the pieces being cracked and chipped. Also, as Tortoise was very ticklish, he would not keep still, so Hare and Tortoise did their best under very difficult circumstances.

So now, if you ever look at a Tortoise's back, you will see that they all have crissed-crossed shells, because of the day poor Tortoise fell from the party in the sky. He has never quite recovered from the fall, so now he and all other Tortoises walk very, very slowly. Oh, and they've all gone completely off chocolate ice cream! If you dare mention chocolate ice cream – watch out! Now you know the reason why – don't you?

Sandra A. Agard

The hazel stick

Well, you know when Adam and Eve were cast out of Paradise, they were pretty upset about it. They had to learn to dig and delve and do all kinds of things, and naturally they didn't like that at all. Adam, especially, kept on moaning and moping and complaining to God that it wasn't fair. And in the end – well, you know how it is when you go on and on and on about something – God gave in, and took pity on him. So He gave Adam a stick made out of hazel wood, and He told him to go and dip the end into the river, one, two, three times, and he'd get something good out of it.

Off went Adam, as pleased as could be, to show off the new stick to Eve. Mind you, he wouldn't let her so much as touch it. He'd had enough off her meddling to last him a lifetime, he said, and anyway this was Man's business. When he was sure she was watching, and ready to be impressed, he went down to the river, waved the stick importantly over the water, and then dipped it in. Once. Twice. Thrice.

The water began to boil and bubble, and then it began to *BAA!* and out came a white woolly head, two horns, four hooves, and a fat body in between. It was a sheep, the very first sheep ever. Adam was absolutely delighted with himself. Straight away he could see how useful the new creature could be.

'Look after it well,' he said to Eve. 'From its back we'll get wool, to spin and weave into cloth that will keep us warm. When we're hungry we can kill it, and we'll get plenty of meat and fat from its body. And from its horns we can made cups for drinking, and spoons for eating with. Truly this is a wonderful beast.'

Now Eve, she listened, and she looked, and she nodded her head, but deep down underneath she wasn't happy at all. Do you know what she was thinking to herself every time she looked at that sheep? She was thinking, 'Mmmm. Now here's a creature Man has made. But who will have to look after it? Woman will! And who will have to take the wool and spin it, and then weave it into cloth? Woman will! And who will have to take the meat from its body and cut it and cook it and serve it up too? Woman will! And who will have to take the horn cups and spoons and wash them after they're used? Woman will! It seems to me this creature Man is so pleased with will be nothing but trouble ever more to us women.'

The more she thought about it, the more she was determined to do something. So that night, when Adam was asleep, she got up and took the hazel stick from above the door, where he'd put it out of reach. And off she went to the river.

'Now let's see what Woman can make,' she said. Just like Adam, she dipped the stick into the water. Once. Twice. Thrice.

The water began to boil and bubble and then it began to *HOWL!* and out came a sleek grey head, long nose, sharp teeth, four paws and a long shadowy body. It was a wolf, the very first wolf ever. And as soon as that first wolf saw the first sheep, it licked its lips and leapt towards it. The sheep didn't waste any time either. With one great bleat it brought Adam from his sleep, to see it disappearing into the distance with the wolf hot on its heels.

Well it didn't take Adam long to work out what had happened, especially since Eve still had the stick in her hands. And I don't think I'd better tell you what he said then – you'll have to imagine that for yourself. But after he'd hurled all the insults he knew – and a few more he'd just made up too – he took the hazel stick and turned back to the river.

'Let's hope this can undo some of the trouble you've caused,' he said, as he dipped it into the water. Once. Twice. Thrice.

The water began to boil and bubble, and then it began to *BARK!* and out came a furry brown head, two bright eyes and a sniffing nose, four paws and a tail that went wag! wag! wag! It was a dog, the very first dog ever. First it licked Eve, then it jumped up at Adam, and then it went off after the wolf. In no time at all it was back with the sheep, looking as pleased with itself as could be.

Adam and Eve patted it on the head.

'You see,' said Eve, 'everything turns out right in the end. After all, if I hadn't made wolf, you'd never have thought of making dog. And wouldn't that have been a pity?'

Adam couldn't quite think what to say to this, so he ended up saying nothing at all. But deep down underneath he was thinking to himself that maybe that hazel stick wasn't such a good thing to have around after all. All that dipping and making, well, you never knew quite where it might lead.

So there and then, he took the stick and snapped it over his knee. He threw the pieces into the river, and they watched them float away. And that was the end of that, as far as they were concerned.

But as for the pieces of hazel stick, they drifted on their way. And where they stopped, and what happened then – well that's another story.

Helen East

The Man in the Moon

There was once a little girl who was as pale as a moonbeam. Each summer she would keep her lonely watch over her family's reindeer herd, far from the village. And when winter came, bringing cold frost and snow, she would drive the reindeer to pastures new. Only when her food ran out did she return home, riding a sturdy buck reindeer.

On one such night, she was riding back to camp when the buck deer cried, 'Look, Mistress, the Man in the Moon is coming!'

As the girl looked up, she saw the Moon Man descending to earth in a reindeer-drawn sleigh. She was afraid, for she knew he would carry her off should he catch her.

'What am I to do?' she cried.

Without a word, the buck deer racked away the snow with his hoof until he had scooped out a large hole.

'Come, hide in this hole, quick,' he said.

The girl hopped down into the hole, and the deer swiftly kicked snow over her head so that soon she was completely covered. All that remained was a mound of snow.

The Moon Man came down from the sky, reined in his sleigh and walked all around, glancing about him for the girl. He even went up to the mound of snow, sniffed at it, listened to it, peered at it – yet never guessed what it was.

'Wherever can she be?' he muttered. 'I cannot see her anywhere.'

With a sigh, he climbed into his sleigh and rode back up the dark curtain of night into the sky.

The moment he was gone, the buck deer scraped the snow from the girl and out she sprang.

'Come, we must go to the village quickly,' he said, 'for the Man in the Moon will surely return.'

The girl clambered upon the reindeer's back and off they rode in a swirl of snowflakes. In no time at all, they reached the village and the girl hurried to her family's walrus-skin tent. Alas, no one was home. Who could save her now?

Again, the buck deer came to her aid.

'I'll turn you into a block of ice so the Man in the Moon cannot find you,' he said.

'No, no, that won't do,' she replied.

'A hammer then.'

'No, that won't do either,' she cried.

'A tent pole.'

'No.'

'A hair on the tent flap.'

'No, no, no.'

Then she had an idea.

'I know, turn me into a lamp.'

As she crouched in the shape of a lamp, the deer struck the ground with his hoof and, in an instant, the girl was turned into a lamp. It burned brightly, lighting up the tent and casting flickering shadows upon the walls.

Meanwhile, the Man in the Moon came racing into the camp. He tethered his reindeer, entered the tent and set to searching it from top to bottom. He peered in between the tent poles, inside every pot and pan, every hair on the fur hides, every twig under the beds, every knot of the bed planks, every grain of soil upon the floor. Yet she was nowhere.

As for the lamp, he did not notice it at all. For although it shone brightly, the Moon Man's glow was even brighter.

'Wherever can she be?' he kept mumbling to himself.

Finally he gave up and returned to his sleigh. Hardly had he climbed into it than he heard a peal of merry laughter from inside the tent.

'Boo! Here I am, here I am!' the girl shouted, poking her head out.

Straight away, the Man in the Moon came rushing into the tent. But the girl had once again turned back into the lamp. His fury mounting, the Moon Man looked among the ashes of the fire, the windblown leaves, the strands of wool, in every breath of air and even the contents of the chamber pot. But she was nowhere to be seen.

'Wherever can she be?' he cried.

Again he gave up. Yet no sooner had he left the tent than the girl grew bold and poked her head through the tent flap.

'Boo! Here I am, here I am,' she called with a laugh.

In a frenzy, the Man in the Moon fairly tore into the tent to begin his search anew, this time even more thoroughly than before. He turned everything over two or three times, even peering into every sound and silence. Yet he could not find her.

So weary did he become from his frantic quest that he started to wane: his burly figure soon faded away until he could barely move his spindly arms and legs.

Seeing him thus, the girl was no longer afraid. She took her proper form, seized the skinny Moon Man and threw him on to his back. Then she bound his hands and feet.

'Ooooh! Ooooh!', groaned the Moon Man's shadow. 'Let me go, I beg of you. Let me free and I'll turn night into day; I'll measure the months of the year for you. Folk will say, the Man in the Moon divides the year into twelve months for us; and to each one he gives a name:

Moon of the Old Buck
Cold Udder Moon
Warm Udder Moon
Calving Moon
Moon of the Running Waters
Making Leaves Moon
Moon of Warm Sunshine
Velvet Antlers Moon
Moon of Love among Reindeer
First Winter Moon
Muscles of the Back Moon
Shrinking Days Moon.'

'If I let you go you will regain your strength,' the girl said. 'And when the marrow in your bones is fat and strong, you'll come down for me once more.'

'No, no, never, I swear!' cried the Man in the Moon. 'I'll never forget the wisdom of earth maids. You are too clever for me. I promise, I'll never come down to earth again.'

So the girl let him go and he rose high into the sky, at once lighting up the heavens and the earth. From that time on he served the people truly, as he had promised, measuring the months and years, and giving them light by which to see.

James Riordan

The pitch lake

Many centuries ago, the Caribs came to the chain of islands known today as the Caribbean, many years before Columbus, the famous discoverer. They lived peacefully with nature and spent a lot of time weaving, carving and fishing. They tell a story about a place which is called Trinidad today. Many of the Carib people liked to live on the south side of the island; some, however, lived at the north side and for some reason they were much richer and happier than those who lived at the south side. This is where the story begins.

A long time ago, the north side of the island of Trinidad was ruled by a queen called Mam. She was a gentle woman. Her hair was quite grey and her skin was quite wrinkled, but she was the kindest woman anyone had ever come across. Each day she would walk around making sure her people were happy and that they had enough food to survive. However, Mam had a daughter called Indaree, who was the most selfish child you could ever come across. She always walked around pretending she was the queen, ordering people of the village around as though they were slaves. Indaree was vain and prouder than a peacock. Mam tried each day to correct her whenever she did something wrong, but it was no good, Indaree thought she was right all the time.

The Caribs lived a good but simple life. They made pots from red clay, they wove hammocks in which they slept, they made cassava bread to eat, and they hunted only at times when food was needed for the people of the village.

But slowly things began to change. For some reason the queen noticed that the hunters were returning to the village with more and more birds and were stripping them of their beautiful feathers.

'Tell me brave warriors, why are you killing the birds?' she would ask them.

They would then reply, 'We've got to look good. We put the feathers in our head-dresses.'

This answer angered the queen. The warriors were becoming vain like Indaree. 'From now on, no-one is to kill another bird for its feathers. The birds live close to the Invisible One our God, and he's sure to punish us if we continue to kill his creatures.'

Indaree listened to her mother and then turned away. She had no intention of stopping the killing of birds. She loved that feeling of power

she got each time she raised her arrow to the sky and the birds fell.

'My mother may be queen now, but I will soon be the new queen. She cannot tell me what to do. I'll do as I please.'

One day Mam went to see Indaree. 'My daughter,' she said, 'it is time for you to choose a husband. I feel marriage will make you change your selfish ways. I am getting older and I long to see my grandchildren before I die.'

'I do not want to get married, mother,' said Indaree, 'and besides, there's no-one in this village who is good enough for me.'

'Surely one of the brave warriors will be suitable,' said Mam.

Indaree thought for a while, then a smile rose on her face. 'No, mother, I have a better idea. You bring seven of the best warriors to me, and I will give them a task. The one who succeeds in this task, I will marry.'

'What will you get them to do?' Mam asked her daughter, worried that she would get them to do something against the law.

'That, my dear mother, is a secret until the day of my wedding,' said Indaree with a firm look.

Mam was just about to leave Indaree's room when Indaree called her back. 'Oh, and mother, build me a beautiful red clay house, spread bamboo mats on the floor, fresh flowers in the rooms and soft feathers for my bed mattress. And you'll no longer be needing your fine jewels. They'll look much better on my beautiful golden skin than on your wrinkly old skin.'

Mam's heart burnt her as her daughter spat those words at her. Indaree knew how it would hurt her mother to hear those words. Mam turned away in angry silence, shutting the door behind her. She knew Indaree was lovely, her hair black and long, yet she had no right to be so cruel.

The following day, the seven warriors were brought to Indaree. They were all tall and muscular and held their heads up to the sky with pride. But Indaree knew Naz was the man she wanted to marry. He was by far the most handsome out of all the warriors. However, she had never shown that she liked him, even when they played as children in the forest.

'Brave warriors,' said Indaree, 'today I have set you a task. The one who does well in this task will take my hand in marriage.'

All the warriors looked at the beauty of Indaree. Naz, who was by far the most handsome and courageous of the brave warriors, had loved Indaree since they were children playing innocently in the forest. Out of all the warriors, he wanted to marry her the most. Indaree looked at the warriors and told them of the task she wished them to fulfil.

'Out of the village, across the stream, into the other side of the forest, there are the birds of paradise,' Indaree said to them. 'They are the most beautiful birds I have ever seen. You will have the opportunity of seeing them for the first time, but not for long. You will kill them and collect their feathers so I can have them. The man who does this deed successfully, I will marry.'

The hunters looked at one another. They all knew it was against the law to kill the birds, but each of them wanted to marry Indaree. So they all agreed to the task which Indaree had set for them and a different day was given to each of the warriors to go out and kill the birds.

On the seventh day, it was Naz's turn. Instead of crossing the stream straight away, he just happened to notice that, hidden in the forest clearing, there was a hut. Naz went closer to the hut. Full of curiosity, he opened the door. All there was in the hut was a shabby old mattress. But as soon as Naz laid eyes on it, he began to fall asleep.

While he slept, he had the most terrifying dream. One moment all the Caribs from the village were singing and dancing and the next moment they disappeared. Naz awoke with a start.

With sweat pouring from his face, Naz tried to figure out his dream. Then he put it to the back of his mind, thinking it so unbelievable. Naz then crossed the river, entering the other side of the forest. It was then he saw them, the birds of paradise, tail feathers stretching two metres long, of every shade of gold and brown imaginable. With a heavy heart, Naz aimed his arrow at the first bird, and many more after that. He collected the feathers and brought them back to Indaree.

Indaree opened the warrior's bags and realised, after counting all the feathers, that Naz was the one she would marry.

The following day there was a great wedding. Everyone was singing and dancing and making great merriment, all except for Mam. She noticed that her daughter and son-in-law were dressed in bridal gowns made of birds of paradise feathers. She knew that they were the sacred birds.

'Indaree,' she asked, 'where did you get those feathers from?'

Indaree looked at her mother and replied, 'Mother, I got them from the paradise birds. So what? Don't you think they look much better on my dress than on those silly old birds?'

'But the Invisible One, our God, is sure to punish us for this!' yelled Mam.

'Mother,' said Indaree, 'there is no such thing as an Invisible One. All this talk about there being a God has only been made up to scare me. I refuse to believe it any longer.'

Mam nodded silently and walked to her home, leaving the wedding to continue without her.

But that night, something terrible happened. The sky turned black and thunder began to pierce the sky. The earth began to shake and tremble. All the homes of the Carib people fell into holes made by the earthquake. Where the cracks were, deep, black, thick tar spurted out from the bottom of the earth and covered the whole village. The only one who survived was Mam, and she went to live with the poor Caribs on the other side.

If you go to Trinidad today, you will see the Pitch Lake, and you will know what went on there all those years ago.

Paula Sorhaindo

DAFT KINGS AND FABULOUS FIBBERS

You're a liar!

Once Ivan and his two brothers went out into the forest to cut wood for the fire. All day they worked, and at the end of the day they were hungry.

Well, they had an iron pot, they had some meat and water for a stew, and they had plenty of wood for a fire, but they had nothing with which to light it. So they looked between the trees of the forest, and suddenly they saw an old bee-keeper's cottage, miles from anywhere, and outside it was the old bee-keeper himself, smoking his pipe, and bald as a beetroot.

Ivan's eldest brother was the first to go across and speak to the old man: 'Good day, grandfather, I wonder if we could have a light for the fire?'

'Well,' says the bee-keeper, 'first of all you'll have to sing me a song.'

'But I don't know any songs.'

'Then you'll have to step me a dance.'

'But I don't know any dances.'

'Then you'll have to tell me a tale.'

'But I don't know any stories.'

'Well then,' says the old bee-keeper, 'there's no quick in you and you'll get nothing from me!'   And he pulls out his knife and cuts a strip of skin from the eldest brother's back and sends him packing.

So along comes Ivan's second brother, and he didn't know any songs, any dances or any stories either, and it was 'Well then, there's no quick in you, and you'll get nothing from me.' And he lost a strip of skin from his back as well.

So along comes Ivan himself: 'Good day, grandfather, I wonder if I could have a light for the fire.'

'Well, first of all you'll have to sing me a song.'

'But I don't know any songs.'

'Then you'll have to step me a dance.'

'But I don't know any dances.'

'Then you'll have to tell me a tale.'

'Ah,' says Ivan, 'I'll tell you a story, but if you call me a liar, I'll have three strips of skin from your back, and a light for the fire besides.'

And the old bee-keeper nods his head up and down, so Ivan sits down beside him and begins to speak.

'Well,' he says, 'it must have been about the time my grandmother gave birth to my grandfather. I was seven years old at the time, and my grandmother gave me some money to buy some bread and some salt and some eggs and some vodka to celebrate the cutting of my grandfather's umbilical cord....'

'Wait a minute, Ivan,' says the old bee-keeper. 'Are you telling me you were seven years old when your grandmother gave birth to your grandfather?'

'Are you calling me a liar?' says Ivan.

'Oh no, not a lie in your body.'

'Well,' says Ivan, 'off I went to the shop and I bought some bread and some salt and some eggs and some vodka, but on the way home the eggs hatched, and out leapt chickens, and they attacked me and overwhelmed me, and they stole the bottle of vodka and set off with it up a tree. Well, I followed them higher and higher, and I could hear them singing and gulping back the vodka, until at last I came to the floor of heaven....'

'Wait a minute,' says the bee-keeper. 'Are you telling me you followed a bunch of drunken chickens up a tree to the floor of heaven?'

'Are you calling me a liar?'

'Oh no, not a lie in your body.'

'Well,' says Ivan, 'when I got to heaven I found that cows and calves were going cheap, and flies and mosquitoes were expensive, and so I climbed back down the tree and filled one sack with flies and another with mosquitoes. Then I climbed back up and did deals with the sinful mortals in heaven. For every fly I got a cow, and for every mosquito I got a calf....'

'Wait a minute,' says the bee-keeper. 'Are you telling me you traded flies for cows with sinful mortals in heaven?'

'Are you calling me a liar?'

'Oh no, not a lie in your body.'

'Well then,' says Ivan, 'when I'd got a beautiful herd of cattle I went to drive them down the tree, but the tree had vanished and there was only yawning space below me. What could I do? Then, suddenly, I remembered the knife in my pocket, so I took it and cut the tails from all those cows, and I tied them together into a rope of tails and lowered it down from the floor of heaven. Then I killed a flea, skinned him and made myself a flea-skin bag. I drove all the cattle into the flea-skin bag, slung it over my shoulder and set off down the rope of tails....'

'Wait a minute,' says the bee-keeper. 'Are you telling me you drove a whole herd of cattle into a flea-skin bag?'

'Are you calling me a liar?'

'Oh no, not a lie in your body.'

'Well then,' says Ivan, 'when I got to the bottom of the rope of tails, I was still two miles above the ground, and the wind began to blow, and I swung first this way, and then that way, and then the rope of tails broke and I fell down, down, down out of the sky and landed up to my neck in rock. What could I do? Then I remembered the knife in my pocket, so I edged my hand down inside the rock, and pulled the knife out and up and I cut off my head and sent it to fetch help....'

'Wait a minute,' says the bee-keeper. 'Are you telling me you cut off your own head and sent it to fetch help?'

'Are you calling me a liar?'

'Oh no, not a lie in your body.'

'Well then,' says Ivan, 'off went my head, rolling along the road shouting for help, when who should jump out of the bushes but an old dog fox. He grabbed my head between his teeth and set off with it across the fields. Well, when I saw that I was furious, wouldn't you be, and I burst out of the rock and started chasing him. I chased him from the west to the east and back to the west again, and when I caught up with that old dog fox I gave him such a kick, I kicked six little baby foxes out of his body. And he lay on his back with his legs in the air, and he opened one eye and looked at me, and with his dying breath he said: "You know, Ivan, there's only one piece of meat in this world fouler than your tousled, tangled, mangled head, and that's the flea-bitten, moth-eaten, bow-backed, dangle-bellied body of the bald-headed bee-keeper of the forest...." '

'You're a liar!'

'Are you calling me a liar?' says Ivan.

'I am calling you a liar, Ivan!'

And Ivan smiles then, and he takes out his knife and cuts three strips of skin from the back of the old bee-keeper, and he takes a light for the fire besides.

And he goes back through the trees to where his brothers are waiting, and they light the fire and put the pot over the flames. And when that stew is cooked, then the real stories can begin!

Hugh Lupton

Master of All Masters

If you wanted a job in the olden days you did not go to the Job Centre! You went to the market place, to the hiring fair. Young boys or girls who wanted to be servants would be tested for health and strength, and then if they were lucky, hired for a job of work.

One young girl called Katie went to the fair. She waited all day but nobody hired her. She was just about to go home, when up came a coach drawn by four black horses. Out stepped a very large gentleman, richly dressed in a black top hat.

'Do you want a job, little girl?' he asked.

'Oh, yes please, Sir,' said Katie.

They travelled in the coach, up a hill to a huge mansion. Inside the house the important gentleman spoke.

'Now girl, if you want to work for me there are a few things that you must learn. Everything in my house has its own special name. What, for instance, would you call me?'

'Oh, I would call you Sir, Sir!'

'Wrong! You will call me MASTER OF ALL MASTERS.'

'Yes, Sir... oops, sorry, Sir, I mean Master of All Masters, Sir.'

'What about this four-poster bed?'

'I would call it bed or couch.'

'Wrong! You will call it my BARNACLE.'

Then he pointed at his smart black trousers.

'What would you call these?'

'Trousers or... pants.'

'Pants! Certainly not, these are my SQUIBBS AND CRACKERS.... What would you call this little cat here?'

'Cat or kit.'

'No, she is WHITE-FACED SIMMINY.'

Then he pointed at the grand fireplace. 'And this?'

'Fire or hearth.'

'Wrong! You will call it HOT COCKALORUM.... And this bucket of water?'

'Bucket or wet.'

'You will call it PONDALORUM.... And now for the whole house?'

'Castle or palace, Master of all Masters.'

'Wrong! You will call it HIGH TOPPER MOUNTAIN.'

Then he showed her a little bedroom and she soon fell fast asleep. But in the middle of the night she was woken by the smell of smoke and a strange crackling sound. She leapt out of bed and rushed into the Master's bedroom. He was snoring loudly. She shook him and shouted.

'MASTER OF ALL MASTERS, GET OUT OF YOUR BARNACLE AND PUT ON YOUR SQUIBBS AND CRACKERS. WHITE-FACED SIMMINY

HAS A SPOT OF HOT COCKALORUM ON HER TAIL, AND IF YOU DON'T GET SOME PONDALORUM, HIGH TOPPER MOUNTAIN WILL ALL BE ON HOT COCKALORUM!'

But the message took so long to deliver, they just had time to run out of the front door when the whole house was burned down to the ground.

Do you know what the message was?

Pomme Clayton

The king who liked a good yarn

There was a king. A horrible man he was – a thief and a bully. He had stolen his kingdom and he bullied his people. He gave himself great airs; and his courtiers, who were every one of them crawlers and toadies enjoying a bit of the king's enormous wealth, were afraid to contradict him. They certainly never mentioned the fact (which they all knew) that his father had been a simple farmer. That might have cost them their lives, because he was very ashamed of the fact.

What the king liked most of all was stories. Great monstrous lies. 'There's nothing I like better than a good mighty fib,' he said. 'And I'm offering the reward of a bowl of gold coins to anyone in the country who can tell me a real unbelievable porky.'

Well, several people tried – but the king, who liked to hang on to his cash, pretended to believe the lies people told him. The dreadful result of this was that he had their heads cut off. 'You're saying that there's a man in the moon,' he'd shout, 'and that he crumbles up the stars to make snow! Why, of course there's a man in the moon. I've seen him myself. And he probably does do that, what you said, to make snow. Off with his head!'

And the unfortunate storytellers were taken away and dealt with. Mostly they bribed the courtiers and escaped with their lives. But no one ever got the bowl of gold coins.

Then, one day a young farmer came to the palace. 'I hear the king likes a good story,' he said. 'My name's Charley and I've come to tell him one.'

He was brought into the main hall, where the king was sitting at a table with a gang of his hangers-on, the courtiers. They were drinking wine and playing cards, amid much shouting and laughter. As Charley came in, the noise died down.

'What do you want?' said the king.

'I've heard you like a good story, your majesty,' said Charley.

'I do. I do,' said the king.

'Well I've come to tell you one.'

'It's not true, is it?' said the king.

'Certainly not, your majesty.'

'That's good, because I only want to hear a good glorious lie.'

'Yes. I know that.'

'A lie. A fib. A porky. A falsehood. A cock-and-bull story. A whopper!

Do you get me?'

'Yes, your majesty.'

The king emptied his drinking bowl. He took out a small sack of gold coins, sovereigns and nobles, crowns and guineas, pieces of eight and ducats, and Charley watched as he poured them into the bowl.

'Not quite full,' said the king.

He took a handful of half-guinea pieces from his pocket and poured them on top, till they were heaped over the rim of the bowl.

'There's a nice lot of money there,' the king said. 'It will all be yours if you tell me a good delicious lie. But,' he went on, unbuckling a sharp-looking sword from his belt and placing it on the table, 'if you *don't*, your neck will taste this.'

And he roared with laughter. All the courtiers laughed too. It seemed to be expected of them.

'All right,' said Charley.

'All *right*,' said the king. 'Begin.'

He leaned back in his chair, his expression stony, his eyes watchful.

'I was off to do a bit of planting the other day,' Charley began, 'when I noticed it was coming on to blow. The wind got up and blew so hard that I got and sheltered behind Dobbin, my horse. It blew harder and harder still, and at last it blew poor old Dobbin in half.'

'What happened then?' said the king, interested in spite of himself.

'Well, the front half sat down, your majesty. And the back half ran round and round the field, whinnying and neighing as it went.... Well, it was scared, you see.'

The courtiers fell about laughing. 'Brilliant! Give him the gold,' they said.

But the king did not smile. 'No,' he said. 'These farmers are clever chaps. It probably happened exactly as he says. Go on, my man.'

'Well, there were lots of daisies in the field, so I made a nice long daisy chain, and with the aid of a pine needle I was able to use the daisy chain to sew Dobbin back together.'

The courtiers all laughed again, but the king said, 'Clever, these farmers. I don't doubt it at all. Go on.'

'Well, at that moment a huge whirlwind came and blew Dobbin up into the sky and he landed on a cloud and stood there, stamping his hooves and tossing his mane. So I thought I'd go up after him. At that moment a great eagle flew by. I caught hold of its legs, climbed on to its back and up we flew. Well, it flew higher and higher and higher and it wouldn't stop till we'd reached the sky. I got off, because I'd noticed a little blue door (almost invisible from down here). I knocked and a couple of angels answered and asked me what I wanted. I told them I was looking for Dobbin, so they said I'd better come in and have a look round, though they hadn't seen any horses thereabout.'

The courtiers laughed.

'What was heaven like?' asked the king.

'A bit like this palace, your majesty, only everything was blue.'

The hangers-on laughed. The king, though, put on a solemn face. 'Yes. It would look like that,' he said, tapping with his fingers on the hilt of the sword. 'Go on. What was happening?'

'The saints were drinking wine and playing cards.'

'Give him the gold!'

shouted a courtier. 'Saints! Playing cards and drinking wine!'

'Why shouldn't they?' said the king. 'I play cards with you. We drink wine. Why not the saints? They're no better than us. Go on, peasant.' He helped himself to a large draught of the good red wine.

'Well, I had a look round for Dobbin but he wasn't there. I'd got a bit hungry, so one of the saints made me a sausage sandwich....'

'Ha-ha-ha,' laughed a courtier. But the king just frowned and began to play with the sword.

'...with a splash of tomato sauce. Well, after I'd eaten it, I got a bit bored, so I decided to go home, but I couldn't think of any way to get down. Well, all this time the whirlwind had been blowing and it had blown a lot of dust up to heaven. So I got to work and plaited the dust into a rope.'

'You can't plait a rope from dust,' said a courtier.

'I don't know,' said the king, whose face had begun to flush with the wine he had been drinking. 'These farmers are remarkably clever. I wouldn't put it past him at all. Go on, farmer.'

'Well. When the rope was a mile long, I looped one end on to the door handle and climbed down the rope. Unfortunately it wasn't long enough, and I found myself dangling a good mile above the field.'

'What did you do?' asked a courtier.

'I took a pair of scissors out of my pocket and cut off the top bit, tied it on to the bottom bit and that gave me another good length and I climbed on down.'

'You couldn't do that,' shouted two or three of the courtiers.

'I'm not so sure,' said the king. 'These farmers are very bright. Go on!'

'Well, the rope was still too short and I was dangling about twenty metres above the field. My wrists and arms were so tired that I just let go. I fell, and landed straight into the field, feet first. I was buried up to my neck with just my head showing. I couldn't move.'

'What happened then?'

'Fortunately I wasn't far from home. So I ran to my barn and got a spade and ran back and dug myself out. Just in time.'

Well, when the courtiers heard that, they laughed and laughed. 'Give him the gold,' they said. 'He's earned it,' fully believing that the king would have to pay up now.

But he wasn't keen to lose all those coins and he said, his face now very flushed, 'Clever these farmers. Far too clever. It may well be true. Have you finished, farmer?'

'Not quite, your majesty. There had been a shower of rain and Dobbin had come down with it on another farmer's land, so I went to fetch him. The weather had turned fine and it was a lovely sparkling day. I came to a farmyard and there I saw a man cleaning out a cow-shed. He was a dreadful sight, up to his knees in cow-muck, unshaven and dirty. But I didn't mind that. "Good morning to you, peasant," I cried, "Lovely day." "I'm not a peasant," he answered, "I'm the king's father."'

At this the king leapt up from his seat, his eyes flashing with anger. 'You liar!' he yelled. 'My father never worked on a farm in his life!'

'No, your majesty, of course he didn't,' said Charley.

The courtiers looked at one another, but kept quite silent.

'Never in his life!' repeated the king.

'No, your majesty. I was telling your majesty a mighty lie. A fib. A porky. A falsehood. A cock-and-bull story. A whopper.'

At that the king, greatly against his will, handed over the bowl of coins.

'Thank you, your majesty,' said Charley, and after a quick bow, first to the king and then to the courtiers, he left the palace with his pockets bulging with gold, his reward for telling a terrible lie (or the terrible truth).

Gerard Benson

Feathertoes

There was once a young Iroquois boy whose name was Feathertoes. Now this was a rather unkind name, because Feathertoes was a little fat and not good at running and jumping like the other children and they used to make fun of him. His mother and father were dead and he was brought up by an uncle who didn't care for him very much, and poor Feathertoes was very unhappy. His only pleasure in life was to look up at the birds and dream that he could fly, just like them.

Now one day, when the other children had been teasing him, Feathertoes ran away from the village and climbed as high as he could into the branches of a tree. He climbed as high as he could and settled himself down on a branch and closed his eyes and began to drift.

But then the wind began to blow on him, and it blew harder and harder, until it blew him right out of the tree! But, to his amazement, he didn't fall to the ground. He put out his arms and he found that he could fly! And he flew around and around, laughing and laughing. At last his dream had come true, and he could fly as well as any bird.

But then the wind began to blow again, and it blew harder and harder, until Feathertoes found that he couldn't fly against it any more, and the wind carried him away and away and away and when it died down Feathertoes came to rest on a little ledge, high on a cliff-face. He was just resting there when he heard a voice, calling to him from the bottom of the valley.

'Feed me!' called the voice.

Feathertoes peered over the edge of the ledge and saw, way, way down at the bottom of the cliff, an enormous face in the rocks beside the river. It was the Rock Man who was calling out to him.

Feathertoes looked about him and found some corn growing on the ledge. He picked it and threw it down to the Rock Man.

'Feathertoes, Feathertoes, come here!' called the Rock Man and Feathertoes stepped off the ledge and put out his arms and floated down through the air and landed beside the Rock Man.

'Feathertoes,' said the Rock Man, 'I have called you here because although it is true that you're no good at running and jumping like the other children, yet you have the best pair of ears of all the Iroquois. Listen to my stories and you will be a great storyteller.'

So every day, Feathertoes would fly down to the Rock Man and the Rock Man would tell him his stories, and at night Feathertoes would fly back up and sleep on the ledge. And it went on like that for many days, until one day Feathertoes woke up and he was freezing cold. He looked over the edge of the ledge and he saw that the face of the Rock Man was all covered in ice. And he knew that there would be no more stories until the Spring. He found that he couldn't fly any more. Wearily, he climbed up the cliff and started walking, searching for a village that he might stay in for the winter.

All day he walked, but when evening came he had found no village, and cold and tired and hungry he settled himself down under a big tree and tried to sleep. But as he lay there, he heard a sound that made him jump. It was the roar of a panther. Feathertoes' heart froze. Could this be the panther that had been killing and eating people from his village? He climbed as high as he could into the tree. He knew that this was no defence against the panther, for the panther could climb any tree better than he, but he couldn't think of anything else to do. He sat up in the tree trembling with fear as the panther came closer and closer.

The panther had his scent now and with a roar it came bounding to the bottom of the tree. The panther reached up one paw and dug his claws into the tree. He reached up another paw, dug his claws in and started to climb the tree.

'What can I do? What can I do?' thought Feathertoes. 'I haven't even got a knife to defend myself with.'

But then he remembered one of the stories that the Rock Man had told him, and in his bravest voice he called out, 'Oh, there's no need to bother climbing the tree, panther. I'm coming right down. By the way, are you the panther who ate my father?'

Now the panther had never been spoken to in this way before and surprised, he stopped climbing the tree.

'Er, no, I don't think so,' said the panther.

'Oh, well, it was probably your father then, or your uncle, certainly one of your relatives anyway,' said Feathertoes, 'but ever since my father told me about being eaten by your father, or uncle or whoever it was, I've been really looking forward to being eaten by a panther. But before I come down, perhaps you'd like to hear the story?'

The panther withdrew his claws from the tree and sat down.

'Er, yes,' he said. 'I think perhaps I better had.'

'Well,' said Feathertoes, 'it's like this you see. Both my father and I are wizards and one day my father was walking along when he met your

father, or uncle or whoever it was, and your father wanted to eat my father. Now my father had never been eaten before and he thought it would be a rather interesting experience, so when your father opened his mouth to eat my father, my father said his magic word, shrunk down to the size of a pea, and jumped into your father's mouth. He slid down his throat and landed in your father's stomach, where he made himself at home. He stopped up a few draughts and made himself comfortable.

'Your father, having eaten my father, found that he was just as hungry as ever he was and he went hunting again and pretty soon he caught a rabbit, which he ate. My father was delighted! It seems he not only had a nice warm place to live, but food was to be provided as well. My father made a small fire in your father's stomach, roasted the rabbit and ate it.

'Your father, having eaten my father and the rabbit, found that he was just as hungry as ever he was, and he was feeling extremely hot! And why was smoke coming out of his nose and his ears? He went and almost drank a lake dry trying to put out the fire inside him, but my father just built himself a small boat and rowed around quite happily in your father's stomach.

'And it went on like that for quite a while, panther, with my father having a wonderful life and your poor father getting hotter and hotter and hungrier and hungrier, until one day my father decided to go back out into the world. He said his special magic word and your father opened his mouth, my father jumped out, took on his own form and went his way.

'A while after that, my father met my mother and they fell in love and got married. And one day, when winter was coming on, they were walking around looking for a place to live, when they met your father.

'Well, when my father saw your father, he turned to my mother and said, "My dear, our troubles are over. Here is a wonderful place for us to live. And we get free food as well."

'When your father saw my father he clenched his teeth shut and said, "I'm not going to eat you, I'm not, I'm not."

' "Oh yes you are," said my father.

' "Oh no I'm not!" said your father.

' "Oh yes you are," said my father, and he said his special magic word, your father opened his mouth, my mother and father shrunk down to the size of peas, jumped into your father's mouth, slid down his throat and made themselves at home in your father's stomach.

'And there they lived for quite a while. In fact, panther, I myself would have been born in your father's stomach, had my mother not wanted to live somewhere with a garden! Well, to tell you the truth, I'm rather cold and hungry up this tree and I'm really looking forward to being eaten, so if you're ready, I'm coming down now.'

And Feathertoes climbed gingerly down the tree, and when he got to the bottom, to his great relief, there was no sign of the panther anywhere!

Feathertoes set off walking, and pretty soon he came to a village. The people came out to meet him.

'Who are you?' they asked him.

'My name is Feathertoes,' he replied, 'and I am a storyteller.'

'A storyteller!' said the people and they invited Feathertoes into the village and gave him a place to live and food to eat and he stayed with them all winter.

Tim Bowley

The king who lost his queen

In the days when pigs could fly and trees barked back at dogs, there lived a king who was so rich that he had grown bored. He had bought everything that money could buy and many things more besides and finally he had grown bored.

He was bored with bathing in his golden bath of asses' milk.

He was bored with being driven in his fur-lined winged chariot.

He was bored with feasts and festivals, with eating the tongues of peacocks stuffed with black truffles.

He was bored with counting his cartloads of cash.

He was bored with his courtiers being so courteous and he was bored with everyone always agreeing with him.

Whatever he said, he was always right. (Nobody dared disagree with him, for years before he had chopped off the head of anyone who crossed him but this had been forgotten.)

He was so bored that half the time he could not keep his eyes open. In the end the Queen sent for the wisest woman she knew and asked her what could be done to help the King.

'What your husband needs is a challenge,' said the old woman, clacking her teeth and sucking her cheeks.

In the dark of the night the Queen and the Princess crept into the King's bedroom and, while his snores shook the rafters and shuddered the timbers, they took off his royal pyjamas. The dressed him in the dirty rags of a cowhand, carried him out of the palace and laid him gently in one of the royal carriages.

When the King woke the next morning he had quite a shock. He was lying on straw in a cow shed. He could smell the most awful smell and after a while realised that it was himself. He called for the royal dresser but only a cow answered.

'Ah,' said the red-faced farmer peering at him, 'so the new cowhand has decided to wake up. Look lively there, the cows need mucking out,' and he flung a shovel at the King.

Twenty minutes later the King had had his first taste of shovelling muck. His hands were blistered, his shirt was stuck to his back with sweat, his feet were covered in cow's muck and yet he had never felt better.

'Right,' roared the farmer. 'Get down to the turnip field and dig up enough to fill two sacks and be back by midday or your name won't be worth nothing.'

The King nodded and, picking up the sack and a spade, went out of the cow shed. Half an hour later the farmer came back to the cow shed and found the King standing by the side of the lane.

'I thought I told you to get down to the turnip patch,' growled the farmer between bitten stubs of teeth. 'What in the devil's name are you doing here still?'

'Waiting for my carriage,' replied the King. (It must not be forgotten that the King had never walked anywhere and had not realised that he would have to walk.)

'Oh,' snarled the farmer looking rather nastily at the King. 'And I suppose your Majesty would like his nose powdered before he goes, eh?'

'Quite so,' said the King, leaning forwards and offering his nose for a gentle powdering. The next thing he knew was that a tornado had smacked him on the nose and he was lying on the ground stunned by the blow. He opened his eyes. The farmer was blowing on his knuckles and grinning.

'I am your King,' sniffed the King. 'Fetch me a stool.'

The farmer laughed out loud and spat on the ground.

'That's a good 'un,' he snapped.

'But I am,' replied the King, sitting up in the dust and brushing his ragged shirt as if it were silk.

'If you're the King, then I'm an angel,' said the farmer, spitting on to his boot caps and polishing them on the backs on his trousers.

'Are you saying I'm a liar?' retorted the King indignantly.

'A liar you may be,' replied the farmer, 'but a pretty useless one. You could never tell a lie as well as I can. Coming on as if you were a King. What sort of a lie is that? Beginners' stuff.'

He hitched his trousers up and stared over the fields into the distance.

The King had never been spoken to like that before but he rose to the challenge.

'I bet I can tell a better lie than you,' replied the King. 'In fact I'll bet you any three things of your choice from the palace if you can tell a bigger lie than I can.'

The farmer wrinkled his nose. 'You'll have to do better than that,' he sniffed.

So they held the competition that very day on the village green and the villagers who came were to decide who was the biggest liar. The King began but unfortunately he wasn't used to this sort of game. He'd never made anything up, he never played tricks, nor told riddles or jokes, and stories and tales had passed him right by. He could be relied upon to lie on a couch of the finest duck feathers, but he had never made anything up in his life before. He stammered and stuttered, turning red with the effort.

'I.... There was.... It all began.... No, please.... You see.... I am His Royal Highness.... and I.... errr.'

He shuffled nervously knowing that things were not going very well and suddenly he had an idea. It fired out of him like gunshot. His first and only lie.

'I am the sister of the blind Princess who saw Death die!'

As lies go, not perhaps the greatest nor the finest, but nonetheless it was his first and it was a start. He smacked his lips in satisfaction. It was extraordinary, he thought. He had no idea where it had come from but the extravagant lie had popped into his brain without any effort at all. He felt ten foot tall. The villagers clapped politely and turned to the farmer.

The farmer herumphed, coughed and moved in front of the crowd. He cleared his throat and began. Unfortunately for the King, this man was a well-practised purveyor of the fabulous, well-versed in the art of tongue-twisting, a tormentor of truth, the finest of fibbers, the lowest of liars, a rhymer and riddler beyond compare, whose fame for fibbing was as widespread as his stomach was large.

'There once was a young lad called Mary who set out to lose his fortune. He rode a cart with square wheels and had travelled only two miles backwards when he came to a well. He climbed up the well and at the top found a dumb tailor. The tailor had no hands and sewed buttons at the speed of darkness on to a pile of sheep's clothing. The dumb tailor told the young lad that a priceless treasure worth nothing was to be found if he dug deep into the ground above the golden apple tree.

'So the young lad aged two thousand years old set off on the journey to find the golden apple tree. He had travelled only a long way when he met a donkey juggling with balls of cold fire. The dead donkey led him straight round to the apple tree. Here the aged youth dug a full hole till he found nothing. He packed his holey sack full of emptiness and set off home to where he would be lost. When he did not get there, he sat down standing on someone else's three feet and declared to his purring dog, "Marry me, you beautiful woman and I will make you the happiest sad wife a woman could ever not wish for."'

So the farmer ended his tale with a flourish and a gob of spit high into the air.

The villagers roared their approval, stamping their feet and tossing their caps high into the air. It was obvious who had won.

But it was the farmer who was amazed when the King finally persuaded him to go to the palace for his reward. Whatever could be taken in three loads. The King smiled as the farmer carted away as much gold and silver as could be carried. There was plenty left. It would make no more than a dent in the King's coffers.

But when the farmer led out first the Princess and then the Queen, the King's smile faded. As he sat that night alone in his bedchamber, he looked out across the country. In the distance he could see the flicker of camp fires and he wondered where his family was.

The days spun by into weeks and the weeks became months and the King's loneliness grew into a terrible ache. What a fool he had been! When he had been with the Princess and Queen he had barely noticed them, let alone spent time with them. But now that they were gone, he began to realise that they were worth more than any treasure.

Then a plan came to him – a worm of a plan, a germ of an idea. He would take the farmer on again in another competition. But this time he would play to get his family back and this time he would win.

So he sent out a proclamation across the land for all well-known liars to come to his court so that he might learn how to lie. The months passed and he began to grow a story of the hugest lies that you can imagine. Soon he would be ready to take on the farmer.

Ending 1

Now how the story ends I never knew. For I heard this tale from a man who grew dumb before the story came to an end. As far as I know the king is still growing his fantastic tale of lies. He still needs more ideas for he must be sure of winning this time round. Maybe you know a fib or two to add to his twisted tale of untruths?

Ending 2

So, the King spent a year and a day weaving the wiliest whopper you could ever imagine. When he was ready he took himself to the farmer's village and prepared for the competition. The villagers came to cheer and to jeer. The farmer came to spit and to fib.

And as before, the farmer's tale was a lie that stretched from here to nowhere and twice back again. But the King did not flinch once.

'Before I begin, just remind me of the rules,' said the King.

'OK,' said the farmer, 'The winner is the one who tells the longest lie.'

'Right,' replied the King. 'The longest lie.'

So he began.

'In the days when pigs could fly and trees barked back at dogs there lived a King who was so rich that he had grown bored. He had bought everything that money could buy and many things more besides and finally he had grown bored....'

It was later that evening when the King's tale had gone round four times in the telling that the farmer pleaded with the King to stop.

Pie Corbett

Peapods

Did you hear the story of the two boys born in a peapod?

There once was a King and Queen who had no children. As the King grew older, the more he would say to his wife, 'If only we had some children, then I could die a happy man.'

But however much they wished, nothing happened. It seemed as if they were not to have children.

In the end the Queen took herself to see the Henwife who lived in the forest. The Henwife was a wise woman who might give you a potion or suggest a lotion, to calm or to cure. She listened to what the Queen had to say and gave her two peas.

'Take these and bury them in your garden but whatever you do tell no one what I have said. In a year you should return and see what has happened.'

So the grateful Queen took the two peas and left the old Henwife. As she walked along the lane, she shook the peas in her hand wondering where to bury them. She was afraid that if she buried them in the palace garden someone might find out. The way back to the palace took her right by a fisherman's hut. She crept behind the hut and planted the peas deep into the dark soil. With that, she made her way back to the palace.

The next day the fisherman's wife cried out when she looked outside. A huge pea plant had grown during the night, climbing up the back of their hut.

'Look,' said the fisherman, 'there's only one pod.'

Sure enough, there was only one peapod, but it was as big as a rattle. They plucked the peapod and took it inside. When they moved the pod, they could hear the peas rattling around.

That afternoon, the fisherman's wife heard a strange crying sound, just like a baby's cry, except very faint. She searched the kitchen, looking for where the sound came from, until she discovered that it came from the last place she expected. The peapod. Quickly she opened up the pod and there lying inside were not the peas she had expected to find, but two tiny babies. Twins.

Well, they looked after those two babies as if they were their very own and soon they grew like any other children. But they were so alike that you could not tell them apart. In every detail they were exactly the same. 'Like peas in a pod,' people in the village used to joke. Their mother would smile – little did the villagers know how right they were.

So, the babies grew as big as any other children and soon they were crawling everywhere. Last thing at night, their father would sing them to sleep. He would stand by their cot watching them, trying to tell one from the other. But it was no good. Only his wife was able to tell them apart.

For their first birthday, the fisherman's wife baked a cake and left it on the window sill to cool. That afternoon they would celebrate. But a cry from the back of the house brought her running and instead of two babies there was only one. She searched through the house, she searched in the wood, she searched by the sea's edge. When her husband returned, he took his boat to the sea and searched along the coast, but all that he saw were the seals lolling on the rocks and the gulls wheeling above.

Some of the villagers reckoned that the seals had stolen the boy; some said that a creature must have come from the woods – perhaps it was a wolf, they thought. None guessed that it had been the Queen, coming back to see what had happened a year after she had planted the peas.

The Queen had snatched the child and had run back through the forest to the palace, where she claimed that an angel had visited her and that there had been a miraculous birth. The King did not mind for at last he had what he wanted. A child to love, a little bundle to cherish, a Prince to take the throne when he died.

And the Queen loved the baby as if it were her own. The baby soon forgot where it had come from and learned to love a new mother. But who is to say that when the toddler fretted in his cot late at night he was not missing the sound of the fisherman's voice singing him to sleep or the steady beat of the waves on the shore or the cry of the gulls in the wind.

All would have been well, but as the boy grew his left leg withered. He grew lame and could not run with the other boys. He limped. His father's joy turned sour. The King felt cheated. This was not the warrior son he had hoped for. This boy was nothing more than a cripple. The King feared that there would be gossip, that his people would snigger behind his back. He was ashamed of the boy and with every lame step the boy took, the King's bitterness grew. So it was that the Queen saw her plan turn as sour as stale milk. Soon she too came to resent the boy.

The lame Prince spent his days in the King's stable. There the Head Groom who looked after the horses gave the young Prince jobs to do and chatted to him, for he liked the lad. The lame Prince grew fond of one horse in particular that he cared for – a special white horse.

He liked to groom the horse and feel his soft hair beneath his fingers. For the horse was warm and would nuzzle the boy, searching for sugar or half an apple. They loved each other, those two.

'What is this?' snarled the King when he found out. 'My son loves a horse more than his father!'

The King made his way to the stables and, in a fit of rage, began to beat the horse with a leather whip. CRACK! sang the whip as it snaked across the horse's back. A streak of blood showed.

The lame Prince yelled at his father, 'No!' but the guards held him back till the King had beaten the horse.

When the moon rose that night, the lame Prince led the horse from the palace and into the woods. More used to palace ceilings, the boy stared up through the branches high above him and watched the moon's eye stare back at him. They walked through forest until, too tired to continue, they lay down. The lame Prince slept leaning against the horse for warmth.

When the Prince awoke, he blinked into the sunlight. There was another boy staring at him. The two boys stood transfixed gazing at each other, for it was like looking into a mirror. Apart from their clothes they were exactly alike. Neither knew that they were twin brothers separated years before.

The horse rose and shook out the night's sleep, stretching down to eat some fresh grass, and the lame Prince explained that he had run away from the palace and from his father, the King.

'You must come home with me,' said the fisherman's son. 'My mother will know what is best to be done. Perhaps you can stay with us.'

The fisherman's wife was repairing a fence when she first saw them, coming down the track from the forest. Her heart leapt, for the first thought that occurred to her was that they were alike as two peas in a pod. Surely, it couldn't be the child that had been so cruelly taken away?

When the fisherman returned later that night, he listened to her tell the lame Prince's story of how he had run away from his father. Deep in her heart she felt that this was her son, but how could that be? And what would the King do to them if he found that they had taken in his son? She was torn two ways — one part of her knew that she should keep the boy but the other half feared what might happen if she did.

'Well,' said the fisherman, watching his wife's face by the lamplight as she wrestled with her feelings. 'Let's sleep on this problem and see what the daylight brings.'

But the morning brought nothing and soon the days ran by until it almost seemed as though the fisherman and his wife had never lost their son. For the two boys were so alike and they got on together as if they were brothers.

But gossip and rumour spread through the countryside and the tale grew in the telling of how the fisherman had found his long lost son. By the time it reached the Queen's ears, the tale had grown beyond recognition but she knew in her heart that the child she had once longed for, the child she had grown, the child she had snatched away, had returned to the love of his first mother.

So the Queen sent her huntsmen into the wood with orders to take the boys and to kill them. But when it came to it, the huntsmen could not carry out the dreadful deed for they had children of their own. So the Queen disguised herself and went into the forest. She tempted the boys with a poisonous apple pie and they ate a slice each, not knowing who she was. Can you imagine the misery of the fisherman and his wife to find their sons killed by poison?

So it was that the children were buried. But out of their grave grew a huge pea plant. From the plant dangled one peapod. It was shaped like a rattle and when the fisherman's wife picked it she could hear the peas rattling around inside. Can you imagine how she felt when later that day she heard a tiny crying sound and opened the peapod to find two tiny babies, alike as peas in a pod?

Pie Corbett

NUMSKULLS AND NOODLES

The dragon of Filey Brig

Billy Biter's cottage was perched high on the steep bank above the river. Far below it was the bridge that everyone called Filey Brig. And under Filey Brig lived a dragon, so that the villagers no longer dared to cross the river.

Billy Biter's wife was a right shrew of a woman – nag, nag, nag, all the day long. No wonder poor Billy stayed as long as he could at the ale-house! One evening he stopped on the way home to do a kindness for a neighbour, and she gave him a big piece of parkin to eat on his way home. Lovely parkin it was – oatmeal and ginger and black treacle, rich and gooey as toffee.

Billy set off for home at last, singing as he went and weaving a bit from side to side, for he'd been a long time at the ale-house. It was a dark, misty, moisty night, and very soon Billy lost the edge of the path and caught his foot in a bramble. Down he fell, headlong, rolling and bumping, right to the bottom of the gully. By sheer good luck he landed in the branches of a small tree that broke his fall and kept him clear of the ground. The rock was fiery hot down there and the water hissing like steam.

Right in front of him two great red lights blinked at him like lamps!

'Oh ho!' rumbled the dragon. 'No need to hunt tonight. Let's have a look at my supper.'

Poor Billy shook so much with terror that he dropped his slice of parkin right under the dragon's nose. A long red tongue shot out to gollop it up. But parkin doesn't gollop easily. It stuck to that old dragon's teeth like toffee, but it tasted wonderful.

'Wha-a-d'yer-call-thith?' he mumbled through the goo.

'P-p-p-parkin, sir,' twittered Billy – all cold with fright though his boots were beginning to scorch.

'Parkin, is it?' said the dragon, sucking down the last bit. His tongue went round and round his jaws. 'Then you go back and bring me some more of it. Aaah-

roosh!'

A crumb of oatmeal had tickled his throat, and he gave such a sneeze that it blew Billy right out of his tree and up to the top of the bank again.

Billy tottered home and told his wife what had happened.

'You silly great fool!' scolded his wife. 'Trust you to do something stupid. And if that dragon doesn't get his parkin, I suppose he'll come crawling up here to find it.'

She set to at once to bake the biggest parkin ever seen. Wide as the kitchen table it was, and so heavy she could hardly stagger with it. But carry it she did, for she'd drunk more than her husband had that night and it made her reckless.

'I'll give it to that there monster,' she said. 'You'd be sure to do something daft, you useless hen-witted bag of old bones.'

Well – what do you think? She was so drunk that she lost her footing and toppled right down to the river. And there the dragon gobbled her up.

'Not that she was worth eating,' he grumbled to himself. 'All tough and bony, like an old, old cow.'

Then he smelled the parkin. It had rolled down with the old woman and was just in front of his nose.

'That's more like it!' growled the dragon.

And that was the last thing he ever said! He golloped the parkin into his mouth in one huge lump. He bit so greedily that his teeth stuck into it as if he'd swallowed a barrel of glue.

Billy ran to tell the neighbours, and they rushed down to the bridge with pitchforks and hammers and scythes and knives and brooms and copper warming pans and anything else they could lay hands on. The dragon was furious, but he couldn't bite and he couldn't blow fire. He could only snort at them through the parkin. So he spread his wings and lumbered away down to the sea to wash the stuff off his teeth. All the villagers followed and caught up with him just as he scrambled into the water. They hit him so hard with all their weapons that his head went under the waves, and he drowned there with his jaws still locked in the parkin.

'Though he weren't such a bad old dragon,' said Billy Biter. 'He did *me* a bit of good anyway.'

I've never been to Filey in Yorkshire, but I'm told there's a long reef of rock there running out into the sea, and that's all that's left of that old dragon's bones.

Margaret Greaves

Soap

A long time ago before the days of electricity, there were no such things as washing machines, so people in the countryside had to go down to the river to do their washing.

Bad weather could be a problem, of course, and so it was for Jack's mother, for it had been raining non-stop for weeks and she now had a great pile of dirty sheets and clothing. Well, at last one day the sun came out and she was really pleased. Quickly she got the dirty washing down to the river and dumped it all into the water – and only at that point did she realise that she hadn't got any soap. She didn't want to leave all her wet washing there, and now it was too heavy to carry back to the house. She needed help, but the only person around was her son Jack. Now she loved him and he loved her, but the problem was that he was so forgetful. If you asked him to do any job, even if he really wanted to do it, he'd probably have forgotten it two minutes later. So, on the whole, she tried not to give him jobs, but this was an emergency and she called him over and said, 'Jack, I need some soap. If I give you some money, will you go down the lane to the store, buy a bar of soap there and bring it back to me?'

Jack was really pleased. She didn't often ask him to do jobs, and he said, 'Sure, Mum, sure.'

Then he put his money in his pocket and started to walk off down the lane. His mother still had her doubts, so she called after him, 'Jack, just keep saying to yourself "soap", and then you won't forget.'

So as he walked off, he went along singing:

Soap, soap, soap, soap,
Soap, soap, soap, soap.

Soon he came to a bend in the lane and because it had been raining so much, it was all muddy. As he went round it, his feet seemed to leave the ground and he skidded smack down on to his face.

His hands and his trousers were all muddy, and worse still, when he got up he couldn't remember what he was supposed to say. He walked one way and said, 'There I had it,' then he walked back and said, 'There I lost it.'

While he was walking to and fro saying that, along the lane from the other direction came a very smart gentleman. He had a top hat and wore a long tail-coat. He was carrying a walking stick, and the way he was walking showed just how very important he was. The gentleman was puzzled to see Jack going to and fro saying, 'There I had it. There I lost it.'

So he went close and bent down to listen to him, but Jack didn't see him and they collided. The gentleman's hat went flying and he slipped head over heels covering his best clothes in mud.

He was really mad and he got hold of Jack and said, 'You shouldn't be saying, "There I had it, There I lost it." You ought to say, "Sorry, I didn't mean to do it." You understand?'

Then off he stormed, furious.

Jack just stood there shaking his head. Oh, was that what he was meant to say? So, off he went down the road saying:

Sorry, I didn't mean to do it,
Sorry, I didn't mean to do it.

Then he went around another bend in the lane and saw a woman who had lost her footing and slipped into the ditch which was full of muddy water. She had a basket of eggs and she couldn't get out. When she heard a voice behind her saying, 'Sorry, I didn't mean to do it,' she thought she knew how she had fallen into the ditch, and she turned round and shouted, 'Hey, you!'

When Jack went over to her, she grabbed hold of him and pulled so hard that she got out of the ditch. But Jack went head first straight into the basket of eggs and then into the ditch. He was filthy; he had an egg shell on his ear and mud all over his face. He was dripping wet. The woman looked down at him and said, 'Well, that serves you right. Now you're in and I'm out,' and off she went.

Jack scrambled out of the ditch with water running off him. Now what did he have to say? Oh yes, and he walked off down the lane saying:

You're in and I'm out.
You're in and I'm out.

He came round another bend in the lane, and there he saw a man whose cart had a wheel stuck in a rut caused by the bad weather. While the man was pushing, he heard a voice behind him saying, 'You're in and I'm out.'

The man turned round and grabbed hold of Jack.

'Don't you say things like that to me!' he said. 'You're going to come here and help me. Now you push here and I'll pull at the front and we'll say, "One's out, get the other one out!"'

So Jack pushed and the man pulled, and suddenly the cartwheel came out of the rut and Jack fell flat on his face and got even muddier.

The man went off with his cart, so Jack started walking again. Now what was it he had to say? Oh yes.

One's out, get the other one out.
One's out, get the other one out.

He went on round another bend in the road, and there walking towards him was the biggest man he'd ever seen in his life. He was a giant of a man, and he was blind in one eye; he must have lost it somehow in an accident. Well, this giant heard Jack saying, 'One's out, get the other one out,' so he bent down, got hold of Jack by his jacket and lifted him up until they were face to face. He stared hard at Jack with his one good eye, and it was lucky for Jack that he was a kind-hearted giant, for he just said, 'You shouldn't say a thing like that. You should say, "Good, one's in anyway." Right?'

Then he put Jack down and walked off.

Jack was relieved. And he knew what he had to say now, so he walked along the lane saying:

Good, one's in anyway.

Good, one's in anyway.

When he turned round another bend in the lane, there was the river again, and there was another woman washing her clothes. She was a young woman with twin babies, two little girls about two years old. The baby girls were playing and their mother hadn't noticed that one had just slipped down the bank into the water. Then she heard a voice saying, 'Good, one's in anyway.'

She turned round and the first thing she saw was her little girl, so she rushed and snatched her out of the water. Then she thought that Jack must have pushed her baby into the river and she ran wildly after him. She grabbed him by the back, swung him round, and then stopped. When she looked him up and down, she forgot what she had been going to say. He had egg shell on his ear, egg yolk running down his face, his hair was matted with mud, his clothes were ripped, everything about him was covered in mud. The woman looked at him and said, 'Goodness me, what you need is a proper wash with soap!'

'Ah!' said Jack, and he thanked her and went off saying.

Soap, soap, soap, soap,

Soap, soap, soap, soap.

At the next bend in the road, there was the store. Jack went in, got out his money and bought the soap. Then, somehow or other, I don't know how, he managed to carry it all the way back home.

When Jack's mother saw him coming with the soap in his hand, she was a bit amazed at what he looked like, but she was so pleased because he hadn't forgotten. She said, 'Jack, you are a good boy! I knew you wouldn't forget. Thank you so much!'

Then she took the soap, scrubbed all the clothes, rinsed them and pegged them on the washing line. And after that she scrubbed Jack all over and pegged him on the line as well alongside the clothes.

Tony Aylwin

The three sillies

Once upon a time there lived a man and his name was John. One day he was walking along the road, and the sun was shining, and he was thirsty. And there, beside the road, was a pub. So he pushed open the door, went inside and called to the landlord, 'Landlord, landlord, a pint of beer, please!'

And the landlord called to his daughter Betsy, 'Betsy, go down the cellar and fetch a pint of beer for this gentleman, will you.'

And so down the cellar stairs went Betsy.

Well, John waited and waited and waited, but no pint of beer came.
'Landlord,' he said, 'what happened to my pint of beer?'
'Didn't Betsy bring it to you?'
'No, she did not.'
'Well then, she must be down in the cellar still.'
So down the cellar stairs they went.
And there was Betsy, with tears streaming down her face, howling and wailing, 'Oh dear, oh dear, oh dear, oh dear....'
'What's the matter?' says John.
And Betsy shakes her head, choking on her sobs and spluttering to find the words, 'Oh dear, oh dear, you see I come down the cellar to fetch a pint of beer, and I looked up and I saw that axe....'
And she points up to where an axe is stuck in a beam in the ceiling.
'...And I fell to thinking... oh dear, oh dear, what if one day I got married... oh dear, oh dear, and what if I had five children... oh dear, oh dear, and what if the smallest one of them children had a cat... oh deary me, and what if that cat had five kittens... oh dear, oh dear, and what if, one dreadful day, the smallest one of them five kittens came down the cellar stairs... oh dear, oh dear, and what if, just at that moment, that axe... oh dear... what if it fell out of the beam... and... chopped off the end of its tail... oh dear, oh dear, oh dear.'
Well, John couldn't believe his ears.
'I've heard some unlikely stories in my time, but that must be the unlikeliest,' he said, 'and I've met some silly people but you must be the silliest. In fact,' he said, turning to the landlord, 'in fact, if I was ever to meet three people more silly than your daughter Betsy, I'll tell you what, I'd come right back here and I'd marry her!'
Well, the landlord grinned and he nodded and he shook John by the hand, and Betsy dabbed her eyes with a hanky and smiled through her tears, and she poured John a pint of the best beer. And John drank the beer, climbed the cellar stairs, and set off on his travels.
Well, he travelled here and he travelled there, and he travelled there and he travelled here, and then one day as he was walking through a village, he saw a wonderful sight.
You see, all the rooves of the houses were thatched, and there was one house where the thatch was so old and rotten that grass had begun to grow on it. Now, an old woman had pushed a ladder up against that house, and she was trying to persuade her cow to climb the ladder and eat the grass.
'Go on, Daisy, climb up the ladder,' she was shouting and scolding, 'go on, Daisy, climb up the ladder.'
But have you ever seen a cow climb up a ladder?
She was thumping the cow, and the cow was stamping and champing.
'Go on, Daisy, climb up the ladder!'
'Mooooooo.'
And John stood and he stared and he couldn't believe his eyes, and as he watched he was thinking to himself, 'There's somebody even sillier than the landlord's daughter Betsy, and that makes ONE.'
Well, he travelled here and he travelled there, and he travelled there and he travelled here, and one night he had to stay in a hotel, and as he was lying in his bed he saw a wonderful sight. You see, the hotel was

crowded, and so he was sharing a room with another man, and early in the morning he was woken by the strangest sound.

Boing... boing... boing... 'Bother!'
Boing... boing... boing... 'Bother!'
And John opened his eyes and looked across the room, and there was the other man jumping on his bed, and tied up between the bedposts were his trousers. He was trying to jump into his trousers!

But have you ever tried jumping into a pair of trousers? He kept missing, and he had to climb up on to the bed and try again.

Boing... boing... boing... 'Bother!'
Boing... boing... boing... 'Bother!'
And John lay and he watched and he couldn't believe his eyes. And then he climbed out of bed.

'Excuse me,' he said, 'but there's a much easier way of putting on your trousers than that. You just hold them in your hands like this, put one foot down here, the other foot down there, heave them up, do the button, pull the zip and there you are.'

'What a good idea!' said the other man. 'I never thought of that. For forty years I've been putting my trousers on like this, it takes me hours every morning. But now... it'll take me no time at all!'

And John stood and listened and he thought to himself, 'There's somebody even sillier than the landlord's daughter Betsy, and that makes TWO.'

Well, he travelled here and he travelled there, and he travelled there and he travelled here, and one evening he was walking and he saw a wonderful sight.

You see, there was a full moon shining in the sky, and beside the road there was a pond, and leaning over the pond there was an old man with a long white beard. He was holding a fishing net in his hand, and he kept dipping it in the water and then peering into it.

'I didn't catch her that time... I didn't catch her that time, neither... Nor I didn't catch her that time, neither....'

And John stood and he stared and he couldn't believe his eyes.

'Excuse me,' he said, 'but what are you doing?'

And the old man looked across at John and he shook his head.

'Stranger, a terrible thing has happened. The moon's gone and fallen into this here pond, and I'm trying to fish her out so's I can throw her back up into the sky!'

But have you ever tried fishing for the moon?

The old man was dipping and peering and shaking his head. And John went across and he caught the old man by the arm.

'Look into the sky,' he said, 'and tell me what you see.'

And the old man craned his neck and looked into the sky.

'That's funny, the moon's up there and the moon's down here.'

And John left him standing by the pond in the moonlight, scratching his head. And as he walked away he was thinking to himself, 'There's somebody else even sillier than the landlord's daughter Betsy, and that makes THREE.'

And so it came about that John married Betsy. It was a lovely wedding... I wish you'd been there!

And do you know, John and Betsy had five children.

And do you know, the smallest of those children had a cat.

And do you know, that cat had five kittens.

And do you know, one day the smallest of those five kittens went down the cellar stairs.

And do you think the axe fell out of the beam and chopped off the end of its tail?

Well..................... it didn't!

Hugh Lupton

Ivan Berenekov

There was once a poor old woman, who had only one son. He was simple-minded, had only one eye and his name was Ivan Berenekov. One day Ivan took his poor old horse and his rusty old scythe and went off to work in the fields.

But after he had been cutting hay for a while, he became tired and sat down in the hot sun and, to amuse himself, he began swatting the flies that were buzzing around him. Thwack! Thwack! Thwack! Thwack! Thwack! In a short while, he had a great pile of dead flies beside him. He began to count them and when he reached five hundred, he tired of counting and, getting up, he went over to where his old horse was grazing. On the horse he saw six great, fat, ugly horseflies.

'Hoh, six mighty champions!' he thought. 'Well, I'm not scared of them!'

And THWACK! With one blow he killed them all. He then got on to his old horse and rode home. And when he got there he said, 'Mother, a peasant's life is not for me. I have this day killed six mighty champions with a single blow, plus countless smaller fry. Give me your blessing, for I am going out into the world to seek my fortune.'

So his mother gave her blessing and Ivan Berenekov took an old basket, into which he put his rusty old scythe, then he got on to his old horse and rode off to seek his fortune.

After a while he came to a crossroads and at the crossroads there was a post. He got off his horse, fumbled in his pockets and took out a piece of chalk. On the post he wrote: 'Ivan Berenekov, the mightiest of champions who, with a single blow, killed six mighty champions and countless smaller fry, passed this way.'

Then he got back on his horse and rode off.

Now, a little later, it happened that another great champion, whose name was Ilya Meromets, rode past this same crossroads and when he saw the message on the post he got off his horse, read it and was impressed! He took silver out of his pocket and wrote on the post: 'Ilya Meromets, the great champion, passed this way following in the footsteps of the mighty Ivan Berenekov.'

He then got back on his horse and rode after Ivan Berenekov. When he caught up with him he said, 'Ivan Berenekov, I am Ilya Meromets, the mighty champion. Shall I ride beside you or behind you?'

'Ride behind me,' said Ivan Berenekov.

Now it happened that there was a third mighty champion on the road that day, whose name was Aliosha Popovitch and he too came to the crossroads and he saw the writing of Ilya Meromets glinting from afar. When he had read the inscriptions, he took gold from his pocket and wrote: 'Aliosha Popovitch, the mighty champion, passed this way following in the footsteps of Ivan Berenekov and Ilya Meromets.'

Then he rode on and when he caught up with them, he said to Ilya Meromets, 'I am Aliosha Popovitch, the mighty champion. Shall I ride beside you or behind you?'

'You'd better ask Ivan Berenekov,' answered Ilya Meromets. 'He is the mightiest champion of all.'

So Aliosha Popovitch rode up to Ivan Berenekov and asked him whether he should ride beside or behind them.

'Ride behind us,' replied Ivan Berenekov.

So the three rode on, until they came to the garden of the King of Prussia and there they decided to camp. Ilya Meromets and Aliosha Popovitch put up their fine white tents and Ivan Berenekov searched in his basket, found an old pair of knickers, which he hung on a bush and lay down under that.

Now, the King of Prussia looked out of his window and when he saw these three camping in his garden, he sent his servants to find out who they might be.

They went up to Aliosha Popovitch and asked him, but he replied, 'You must ask Ilya Meromets.'

But when they asked Ilya Meromets, he replied, 'You must ask Ivan Berenekov, for he is the mightiest champion of all champions and has killed six mighty champions with a single blow.'

When they asked Ivan Berenekov, he said, 'We are Ivan Berenekov, Ilya Meromets and Aliosha Popovitch and we are three mighty champions.'

They took this message back to the king and he looked in his book of mighty champions and there he found the names of Ilya Meromets and Aliosha Popovitch but no mention of Ivan Berenekov.

Now it happened that at that moment, Prussia was invaded by the Emperor of China, who had with him six mighty champions and a countless horde of soldiers. The King of Prussia was very frightened and he sent a message to the three champions, asking them to help him and they agreed that they would.

The Chinese Emperor sent a countless horde of soldiers into the attack and Aliosha Popovitch asked Ivan Berenekov whether he would send them or go himself.

'Aliosha Popovitch, you go,' answered Ivan Berenekov.

And Aliosha Popovitch mounted his mighty steed and rode into the middle of the Chinese army, trampling soldiers left and right and centre until they fled from the field.

The Chinese Emperor then summoned his six mighty champions and, together with countless hordes of soldiers, sent them against the King of Prussia. Ilya Meromets came to Ivan Berenekov and said, 'Six mighty champions and a countless horde of soldiers are attacking the Prussians. Will you send us or go in yourself?'

'Ilya Meromets, you go,' said Ivan Berenekov.

So Ilya Meromets got on to his great horse, rode to the field of battle, killed the six mighty champions and drove the soldiers from the field.

'Ahh, this is very, very, very serious,' said the Chinese Emperor, 'But I have a secret weapon. I have one more mighty champion, mightier than all the others. I had hoped to keep him for breeding purposes, but I see I must send him into battle.'

And he summoned this champion and said, 'Listen, my mighty

champion. So far these Russian champions have defeated us by cunning. Whatever their champion does, I want you to do as well.'

This mighty Chinese champion then mounted his enormous warhorse, who breathed fire out his nostrils, and together with a countless horde of soldiers, rode against the king of Prussia.

Then Ilya Meromets and Aliosha Popovitch came to Ivan Berenekov and said, 'The mightiest champion of all, together with a countless horde of soldiers, rides against the King of Prussia. Will you go yourself or will you send us?'

Ivan Berenekov looked up and said, 'I'll go myself. Fetch my horse.'

So they went to fetch the horse of Ivan Berenekov, which was grazing nearby. But the horse did not want to go into battle and tried to kick them. And at this, Aliosha Popovitch lost his temper, grabbed the horse by the tail and threw him over the hedge. Ilya Meromets and Aliosha Popovitch looked at each other in horror!

'I hope the mighty champion Ivan Berenekov did not see us mistreating his horse. Clearly, his strength is not in his horse but in himself.'

They went and caught the horse and brought him to Ivan Berenekov.

Ivan Berenekov picked up his rusty old scythe, climbed on to his old horse and rode off to meet the Chinese champion. And when he was a little way away from the Chinese champion, Ivan Berenekov stopped his horse. Remembering his instructions from the Emperor, the Chinese champion stopped his horse too.

Ivan Berenekov got off his horse, so did the Chinese champion. Ivan Berenekov sat down on a stone and began to sharpen his rusty old scythe. The Chinese champion sat down on a stone and began to sharpen his sword. But then he noticed that Ivan Berenekov had only one eye.

'Aha!' thought the Chinese champion. 'This Prussian champion has one eye closed. I will outsmart him. I will close both of my eyes.'

When Ivan Berenekov saw that the Chinese champion had both of his eyes closed, he crept up behind him and, Ssswwish, cut off his head with his scythe. Then he went up to the mighty warhorse of the Chinese champion, which was tethered to a great oak tree and tried to climb on to him, but the horse threw him off.

Ivan Berenekov climbed the tree, clambered out on to a branch and jumped on to the horse's back. Feeling a rider on his back, the horse began to gallop and he was so strong that he pulled that oak tree out by the roots and began to gallop towards the Chinese army.

'Help, help, help!' cried Ivan Berenekov. 'Whoaa! Stop! Stop!'

But unfortunately the horse did not speak Russian and continued to gallop right into the Chinese army, dragging the great oak tree behind it and with Ivan Berenekov screaming at it to stop. The Chinese soldiers, knocked over by the tree and terrified by the screams of Ivan Berenekov, fled from the field.

The Emperor sent a message to the King, saying that he could not possibly fight against such a mighty champion as Ivan Berenekov and was leaving the country. The king was overjoyed and, as happens so often in stories, Ivan married the king's daughter and as far as I know, they're still living happily together.

Tim Bowley

The lion and the foolish traveller

There was a traveller who made his living by walking from village to village telling stories. The children always looked forward to his visits. In the evenings everyone would gather round the fire and the traveller would hold them spellbound with one story or another. In return the villagers would give him whatever he needed. Sometimes it would be a hat to keep the rain off. Sometimes it would be a shirt to clothe his back. Sometimes, a hot meal was enough.

One day the traveller was walking through the jungle to a village at the foot of the great hills when he came across a lion lying right on the path. He stopped dead still and did some fast thinking. He knew that if he turned and ran the lion would be on him in one bound. And that would be that. So he stood quite still and waited. He had heard somewhere that if you looked right into a lion's eyes you could stare them out. And that in the end the lion would get up and go away. So the traveller stared deep into the lion's amber-brown eyes.

After a while the lion folded its paws together and put its head down. It closed its eyes. The traveller was very excited by this. It's working, he thought. The lion could no longer hold his gaze. He would be known as the man who stared out the King of the Jungle. What a story it would make. The traveller thought to himself that he might now be able to creep away. He was just turning to go when the lion opened its eyes. The traveller stared back at the lion. For a long time they stood like this.

Then the traveller thought that it might be a good idea to copy the lion. So he put his hands together and bowed his head. The lion bowed its head down again. The traveller thought that if he closed his eyes perhaps the lion would too. So he closed his eyes and hoped that the lion would do the same. But when he peeped out of one eye he could see that the lion was still watching him. Then it spoke.

'I don't know what you are doing,' growled the lion, 'but I am saying grace.'

Pie Corbett

Archie's besom

A long time ago in the West Highlands there once lived two brothers called Donald and Archie. They had a small croft between them, a small farm. And there they lived quite happy. But poor Archie – Donald, being the oldest brother, he never gave him a penny. Archie worked all week long, milking the cows, taking in the firewood, taking in the peats for the fire. He cut the hay, he cut the harvest, he clipped the sheep. And all his older brother would give him was a sixpence a week. One single sixpence. Archie, of course, got his food and his clothes. He was quite happy with his sixpence a week. Till one day.

Up on the hillside there was an old farm road that went on for miles. And you know those stone dykes that they build along the side to keep the sheep from getting on the road? Some of the pieces of dyke had been falling down. And Donald said, 'Archie, we'll have to go up today and try and build up some of these parts of dyke, because the sheep are getting on the road. They're travelling for miles.'

'All right, Donald,' Archie said, 'we will go.'

So they went and started patching the dykes to keep the sheep in. When at that moment who should come walking along the road but a tinker man with his bundle on his back. When he came up, he said to Donald and his brother, 'Would any of youse men have a match youse could spare to light my pipe?' And Donald smoked but Archie didn't. So he said, 'Of course!' and Donald gave the tinker man a match. He lighted his pipe.

Now where they were working on the hills was all that beautiful heather, you know. And the tinker man said, 'Do you own all this land here?'

Donald said, 'Of course. As far as you can see, that's our hill for the grazing of our sheep.'

'Well, you wouldn't mind if I could have some of your heather?' said the tinker man.

'Heather?' said Donald. 'Of course, you can have as much as you want. The sheep won't even eat it. What are you going to do with it?'

The tinker man said, 'I am a besom maker. I make heather besoms.'

For sweeping the floor they were very popular in bygone times. These travelling people made heather pot scrubbers and heather besoms. And they were very good at it.

Donald said, 'Help yourself, take as much as you want!'

So the tinker man climbed the dyke and went over and started pulling all that heather to make besoms, or brushes, as they were called for sweeping the floors, sweeping the byres. Archie thought he would go over and see what the tinker man was doing.

He watched him and said, 'What are you going to do with all this heather, tinker man?'

He said, 'I make besoms.'

'Oh I see,' said Archie. 'Are they hard to make?'

'Och no,' he said, 'really not very hard to make. You just take a bunch of heather and put a handle in it, and you tie with some string. And you trim it. And you've got a good brush! You can sweep anything with it, leaves in a garden or a byre or anywhere.'

Archie said, 'That seems very interesting. And how much do you get for one of these things when you make them?'

'Oh well,' said the tinker man, 'maybe a shilling for one.'

'A shilling?' said Archie. 'You mean, you can get a shilling for making a besom?'

'Yes,' said the tinker man, 'that's my job. I'm a besom maker.'

'And how long does it take you to make one of these things, a besom as you call it?' said Archie.

'Oh,' he said, 'maybe twenty minutes if I'm in a hurry.'

'Twenty minutes? A big silvery shilling for twenty minutes?' said Archie. 'And here's me labouring and toiling to my brother all week long for one silver sixpence.'

Tinker man said, 'It's none of my business.'

And he picked up his heather and walked away. Gone was the tinker man.

Archie stood and said to himself, 'Maybe I could become a besom maker.'

And at that very moment Archie made up his mind – he was going to become a besom maker!

And then his brother Donald shouted, 'Archie, come and help me with this stone! It's too big for me to lift by myself.'

And Archie said, 'Indeed not, Donald! I live with you, I'll stay with you but you'll never get another day's work out of me as long as I live!'

But Donald said then, 'What are you going to do for a living?'

Archie said, 'I'm going to become a besom maker, and sell besoms like the tinker man.'

But Donald said, 'Archie, these people are professionals! They know their job. You could never make a besom!'

Archie said, 'At least I can try, can't I?'

So he went over to the hillside and he pulled a large, big bundle of long heather. He carried it back to his little farm house into the byre. And he got a big cromak stick made of hazel, and he cut the handle off. He stuck it into the bundle of heather. And he tied it with a piece of rope.... It was the ugliest looking besom you ever saw in all your life! But Archie was proud of it. It was his first attempt.

Archie said, 'Wait till Donald comes back and sees this. Isn't she a beauty? She's the most beautiful besom.'

He could barely take his eyes off it. So he made the tea for Donald coming back, but he could not wait to tell him.

Donald said, 'Archie, you never came back and gave me a help with the stones to build the dyke.'

'I told you I'm not doing any more work for you, Donald!' he said. 'I have a surprise for you. Come till you see this! You'll never believe it.'

Donald went into the little byre. 'And there,' Archie said, 'look over there against the wall!'

Donald said, 'What's that?'

He said, 'It's a besom of course!'

'A besom?' said Donald. Donald had seen many besoms. In fact he had a few in the house himself, well made ones. 'Archie, that's not a besom.'

'Of course that's a besom!' said Archie. How dare you say that it's not – after me working so hard on it. She's a beauty, isn't she?'

'What are you going to do with it, Archie?'

'I'm going to take it to the village in the morning and sell it,' he said.

'Oh no, Archie,' said Donald, 'you're not taking that to the village in the morning! Please, Archie! Archie, you know I'm a member of the church. And you taking to the village in the morning and trying to sell that – you'll put me to shame.'

'I don't care if you're a member of the church or not,' he said. 'It's going to the village in the morning, and she's going to be sold! And then I'm going to make more.'

'Oh no, Archie, please no, don't make any more!' said Donald. 'Please, I beg of you. Look, I'll raise your wages to five shillings a week.'

'I don't care suppose you raise my wages to a pound a week!' said Archie. 'I'm going to become a besom maker.'

Donald coaxed him all he could. But Archie wouldn't budge an inch. He was going to the village with his besom in the morning.

So true to his word, after breakfast he took the besom on his shoulder – the most ugly, fattest, biggest, untidiest besom you ever saw in all your life! And he walked to the village. And he went from house to house. It wasn't a very large village. And people looked and they said, 'Hm, no.' They would have bought it if it was a nice one, you know. Because besoms were very popular in those days for sweeping leaves and sweeping byres, and people used them in the houses. No, they wouldn't have it. Archie tried every single house in the village. No one would buy Archie's besom. Archie was getting a little bit down-hearted.

'I can't go back to Donald now,' he said, 'and take this back with me. He'll make a fool of me all my life. She has to be sold before I go home somewhere!'

And then he remembered. There was one house he had not gone to. High in the hillside was a little house, and Archie remembered there was someone living there. He said, 'It's worth a try.'

So he walked up the little path with the besom on his shoulder, and he came to a little thatched house up on the hillside. There were hens running around and smoke coming from the chimney, but no one was outside. By this time Archie was getting more down-hearted, so he kept the besom at his back, you know, a little ashamed of it. And he came up and knocked on the door. He waited. And then the door opened.

Out comes this woman. And, boys and girls, believe me, she was only about four foot high, but she was about six foot broad. Every arm she had was like a big ham, you know. Three chins! And her legs were so thick she could barely walk. She just waddled. But she was smiling. She said, 'Well, young man, what can I do for you?'

Archie said, 'Well, you see, I was wondering if you'd be interested in buying a besom?'

She says, 'You mean, a real besom? A broomstick? A heather one?'

Archie said, 'Yes.'

'And you have one for sale?' she said.

Archie said, 'I have.'

'And what would you be wanting for it?'

'Well,' Archie said, 'the tinker man said it's worth about a shilling.'

And he took it in front of him. The moment she looked at it her eyes lighted up. She said, 'A shilling for that beautiful thing? I'm going to give you two silver shillings if you're selling it to me!'

Archie said, 'Done, you can have her!'

So she gave Archie two silver shillings. Archie rubbed his hands in glee and he thanked her very much. He walked down the path to the village. What a story he was going to have for Donald when he got back!

But unknown to Archie or to anyone, the woman in this little house was known as Fat Maggie. And Fat Maggie was a witch! But Fat Maggie could never afford to get a besom big enough to carry her. So she took it into the little room and she put a spell on it. She sat on it and she spun round the room as happy as a lark with her fat legs sitting across it. 'Now,' she said, 'At last I have transport!'

And she rubbed her fat palms in glee.

So, boys and girls, late that night all the witches in the land were holding a meeting in the birch forest many miles away. And they all flew in on their broomsticks one by one. They landed in the birch forest, and they sat in a ring with their broomsticks beside them. They began to talk about things. But the main subject was Fat Maggie.

They said, 'Oh, she's powerful! She's the most powerful witch in all the land. But she'll never get here. She'll never find a besom to carry her weight, never in a million years.'

So this is what they were all talking about sitting in a ring, all these old crones, old witches. When then, it was a beautiful moonlit night and a shadow crossed the sky. They looked up. Here comes Fat Maggie astride Archie's besom.

She looked and looked and she came down. She stopped right in the middle of the ring of witches. And she stepped off. She looked all around her, but she said, 'Youse are always talking about Fat Maggie, aren't you? Oh, she's fat and ugly. She'll never find a broomstick, will she? She'll never get here to join our meetings, will she? But now Fat Maggie's here! And Fat Maggie, as you call her, will be flying home tonight on Archie's besom. But for youse witches – youse'll all be walking!'

So she gathered up all the witches' broomsticks and she threw them into the birch forest. And there they stuck. Fat Maggie flew home that night on Archie's besom. But for the rest of the witches they had to walk.

Now when *you* walk through a birch wood in any part of the West Coast of Scotland, and you see all these things that look like birds' nests on the birch trees. They are not nests at all. They are what we call on the West Coast of Scotland *Witches' Besom*. For Fat Maggie had put a spell on them and there they stuck up in the trees for evermore.

Duncan and Linda Williamson

The man in search of his luck

Once upon a time when the blind were tailors, the legless jumped over walls, and the deaf heard the news all over the world, there was a man who was very unlucky. Not just for a day. Not just for a week. Not just for a month. But for years and years and years. Until he had no roof over his head, no money in his pocket, and only the shirt on his back.

He said to himself, 'Why me? Why am I so unlucky? It must be somebody's fault. Who puts all the luck into the world and takes it out again? God! It must be God's fault. I am going to find God and ask him why I am so unlucky.'

So he set off, asking everyone he met if they had seen God. People pointed to the sky. They pointed to their hearts. Some people just shook their heads.

The man walked for a day. He walked for two, the further you walk, the further you get!

He came to a wolf lying in the road. He was all skin and bone and his tongue was hanging out of his mouth.

'Have you seen God?' asked the man.

'God?' rasped the wolf. 'Can't you see there's no God here? But if you find him, please ask why I am so hungry.'

The man walked for a day. He walked for two, the further you walk the further you get.

He came to an apple tree, without any apples. All its branches were brown and withered and drooping.

'Have you seen God?' asked the man.

'God?' panted the tree. 'Can't you see there's no God here? But if you find him, please ask why I bear no fruit.'

The man walked for a day. He walked for two, the further you walk the further you get.

He came to a little house on top of a hill. It had a tidy garden and roses round the door. A beautiful young woman looked out of the window. She had been crying.

'Have you seen God?' asked the man.

'God?' sniffed the girl. 'Can't you see there's no God here? But if you find him, please ask why I am so sad.'

The man walked for a day. He walked for two, he walked so far, he came to the edge of the world.

There was a sheer cliff disappearing into dark space. Hanging in space was a rock. Sitting on the rock was a very old man, with a long white beard.

'Are you God?' asked the man.

'Yes... yes, some people call me that,' said the old man, twiddling his thumbs.

'Why am I so unlucky?'

'Ah, I have heard about you,' replied God. 'You're the man that has never looked for his luck!'

'What! You mean my luck is out there, waiting for me?'

'That's right,' said God. 'All you have to do is find it.'

The man was so excited. 'I have a few other questions to ask, would you mind?'

'No,' said God. 'Fire away, I have plenty of time.'

So the man asked his questions and then set off as fast as he could.

'I am going to find my luck,' he cried. 'My luck is waiting for me somewhere!'

The girl waved at him from her little house.

'Did you find out why I am so sad?' she called.

'I found out,' he shouted. 'I found out, that I am going to be the luckiest man in the world.'

'But what about me?'

'Oh yes, God says that the reason you are so unhappy is because you're lonely. All you need to do is get married.'

'But how can I do that?' she said. 'I don't know anybody.'

Then she smiled, 'I know, you're a man, would you marry me?'

'Oh no,' said the man. 'I have much more important things to do. I am looking for my luck.'

And he ran off down the hill.

'I am going to find my luck,' he cried. 'My luck is waiting for me somewhere.'

He came to the tree.

'Did you find out?' whispered the tree.

'I found out,' said the man, 'that all I have to do is take my luck and it will be mine.'

'But what about me?'

'Oh yes, God says that the reason you bear no fruit, is because there is a box of treasure blocking your roots. All you need to do is dig it up, and your sap will rise again.'

'But how can I dig it up? I am just a tree. But you are a man, and there is a spade over there. Would you do it for me?'

'Oh no,' said the man. 'I have much more important things to do. I am looking for my luck.'

And he ran off through the forest.

'I am going to find my luck,' he cried. 'My luck is waiting for me somewhere.'

He came to the wolf. His bones were jutting through his flesh, and the edges of his tongue were turning black.

'Did you find out?' gasped the wolf.

'I found out that I am the luckiest man alive.'

'What about me?'

'Oh yes, God says that if you are hungry, you must eat the first stupid man that passes by.'

So he did.

Pomme Clayton

Pwyll and Rhiannon

If you've ever heard of Pwyll[1], Prince of Dyfed, you'll know that he was much like you or I. But something about him there was, which drew to him the Unseen Folk, from the Unseen Country, which some people call the Otherworld. Hear now of such a time.

It was a time when Pwyll was much burdened with the cares that beset a chieftain, and wished to be on his own. He began to walk away from the feast hall towards a great hill nearby, green and waiting, which was called the Throne of Arberth.

As he did so, some of his people ran up to him, and said, 'Lord, there is something you should know about that hill, green and waiting. If a man of noble blood sits upon it he either receives wounds and blows, or he sees a marvel!'

'Well,' answered Pwyll, 'I am no stranger to wounds and blows. Perhaps I'll see the marvel.'

And he went on his way towards the Throne of Arberth.

So some of his people went with him. The moment he sat down at the top of the hill there appeared, in the distance, a figure. They could see that it was a woman on horseback, finely mounted, finely dressed and finely made, but veiled.

'Who knows that woman?' asked Pwyll, and no one answered.

'Well, then, one of you, go and greet her for me.'

There was one among them, known throughout all of Dyfed as the fleetest of runners, and he shot off down the hill, like an arrow fired from a bow.

When he'd reached the road at the bottom she had already gone past, even though her pace was just a gentle trot. So like an arrow fixed a second time, he turned along the road and sped after her. She went on at an easy trot, quite without effort. But he got not closer to her. He ran and ran for all he was worth, but he got no closer to her. He ran until all his strength was spent, but he got no closer to her. In the end, all he could do was drag himself back up to Pwyll like one defeated.

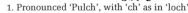

'We saw it all from up here,' said Pwyll. 'No one could have run faster than you. So to the stables, take a horse, and catch up with her that way.'

So the runner took a horse and galloped off after the woman. She went on at an easy trot, quite without effort. But he still got no closer to her. He galloped hard, and

1. Pronounced 'Pulch', with 'ch' as in 'loch'

harder still, but he got no closer to her. And in the end his horse was utterly exhausted, and all he could do was stagger back to Pwyll, dejected.

'Don't blame yourself,' said Pwyll. 'No one could have tried harder. There is some meaning in this.'

The next day they all went back to the top of the hill, but this time the fastest horse in all Dyfed was saddled and bridled for the lightest youth who was capable of riding it. The moment they all settled at the top of the hill, the woman appeared. Immediately, the rider hurtled down the hill. But by the time he'd reached the bottom, she'd gone past, at her easy trot. He dashed after her. But riding hard, he got no closer to her. He rode and he rode until his horse had no strength left, and all he could do was return to Pwyll like one in despair.

'Don't be hard on yourself,' said Pwyll. 'We watched from up here and know you did your best. But this lady means to show herself to someone hereabouts.'

Now the next day the horse was prepared for Pwyll himself. As soon as the woman appeared he was off down the hill. Once more she went past at an easy trot, and he turned to ride after her. Once more, he got no closer to her. He rode on desperately until his horse was ready to drop, and all he could do was call out, 'Lady, for the sake of him you love best, stop!'

She turned and waited.

'Gladly I will,' she said, 'and it would have been better for your horse, and for its rider, and your other horse and rider, and your runner, if you'd asked me sooner!'

I don't know if Pwyll was more astonished than amazed by this, or if he was more astounded than astonished or amazed, but nevertheless he pulled himself together and asked, 'Where are you bound, lady?'

'About my own errands,' said she.

'And may I know anything of these errands?'

'One of them,' she replied, 'is to see you.'

And so saying, she lifted back her veil, and Pwyll knew that he had never seen a face lovelier, in dreams or in waking.

'That errand gives me pleasure indeed,' he said. 'And may I know your name?'

'My name is Rhiannon, and I am the daughter of Hefeydd[2] the Old.'

Now Pwyll knew that he witnessed a marvel indeed, for Hefeydd the Old ruled a tribe of the Unseen Folk, from the Unseen Country, which some people call the Otherworld.

'Know also,' went on Rhiannon, 'that I am to be married to one I would not have. For there is only one I would have, and none other unless he

2. Pronounced 'Hevith'

will not have me.'

'And may I ask,' enquired Pwyll, 'who that would be?'

Her answer was, 'He stands before me.'

Well, whether Pwyll was more astounded than astonished, or more amazed than either of these, he nevertheless just about managed to say, 'By all the stars, I will have you!'

'Then come a year from today,' she said, 'to the hall of Hefeydd the Old, where a wedding feast will be prepared.'

And then she was gone.

The year which now followed was a long one for Pwyll. But at the end of it he found, without delay or difficulty, the hall of Hefeydd the Old, just as if it were in the next valley. Indeed, perhaps it was. He found waiting there a fine wedding feast – fair guests, fine wines, rare meats, and Rhiannon in all her glory. He sat next to her at the high table. He ate well, he drunk well, and he'd never felt better. When his happiness was at its height, there came another guest to the wedding feast.

This guest was tall, princely and auburn haired. He strode up to the high table.

'My welcome to you,' said Pwyll.

'My thanks to you,' replied the other, 'and may I ask a favour?'

Now this was a custom at wedding feasts at that time, and so Pwyll answered, 'Ask, and whatever it is, I shall give it.'

But when he said that, Rhiannon's face fell, like a stone falling into a deep, dark hole. But all she said was, 'Numskull!'

'Indeed,' said the guest, 'but those words he has spoken before all these witnesses. I ask, Pwyll, for your bride.'

To this, Pwyll said nothing.

'Well you may be dumb,' hissed Rhiannon, 'for that is Gwawl[3], rich in lands and followers, whom I was to have married!'

'What can I do?' whispered Pwyll. 'I will not give you up, but I cannot break my word....'

'Tell him,' said Rhiannon, 'to come here a year from today, when a wedding feast will be prepared for him, and in the meantime, I will give you something, and I will tell you something.'

The year which followed was far longer for Pwyll than the year before, for he had lost the one he loved most. But in that year a new Pwyll emerged – saddened, sobered, but sharper. At the end of that year two figures came to the wedding feast at the hall of Hefeydd the Old. One was Gwawl – tall, princely, and shining with triumph. Now he sat at the high table, ate well, drank well and knew this as the happiest day of his life. When his happiness was at its height, the second figure arrived.

He was the shabbiest, dingiest of beggars, covered from head to foot in grey, old rags. His face was hidden by his hood. He shuffled up the length of the hall to the high table.

'My welcome to you,' said Gwawl.

'My thanks to you,' answered the beggar, 'and may I ask a favour?'

For such was the custom at wedding feasts at that time.

'Ask,' replied Gwawl carefully, 'and, as long as what you ask is reasonable, I shall give it.'

'It's very reasonable,' said the beggar. 'Whenever I travel, hunger accompanies me. I only ask that I be allowed to fill this bag here with food

3. Pronounced 'Gwowl' to rhyme with 'Howl'

from your wedding table.'

'That's reasonable indeed,' responded Gwawl, and he gave a sign to a serving man. The serving man brought down a whole loaf and dropped it into the bag which the beggar was holding open. And the bag stayed open. Then another serving man came and dropped in a roast chicken, and the bag stayed open. More serving men came, until there was a long queue of them, waiting to drop food and drink into the bag. And the bag stayed open.

When gaps began to appear on the tables of the wedding feast, Gwawl was alarmed.

'Friend,' he called out, 'will that bag ever be full?'

'Er... no!' said the beggar calmly, 'it won't ever be full. Unless, that is, a man of noble birth puts both feet in the bag and says, "enough has been put herein."'

'Quickly!' said Rhiannon to Gwawl, 'do this, or there will be nothing left of our wedding feast!'

So, Gwawl walked over, he put one foot, then another foot into the bag and said, 'Enough has been... mmpf!'

For the bag was up and closed over his head, and the neck of the bag was securely tied by the beggar, before Gwawl could finish his words. The beggar lifted back his hood from his face and everybody could see that it was Pwyll.

Then he took out his hunting horn, put it to his lips and blew. In an orchard nearby, a hundred of his men were waiting. When they heard the horn, they came into the hall, one by one. As each one came, he landed upon the bag either a blow or a kick.

'What's in this bag?' one would say.

'A badger!' another would answer.

'What game are we playing?' the first would ask.

'The game of Badger in the Bag!' the second would reply. And afterwards a game of that name was played all over the country.

After a time Gwawl's voice could be heard shouting something.

'What he says is true,' said Hefeydd the Old. 'This is not a fitting death for such as he!'

'Well, I know it,' said Pwyll. 'What do you advise me to do?'

'Ask Gwawl,' said Rhiannon, 'to make a pledge, that he gives up all claim to me, and that he will never try to seek revenge for what has happened here.'

'I pledge it!' came the muffled shout from the bag.

So Pwyll unfastened the neck of the bag and Gwawl began to pull himself free, extracting the pie crusts and other bits of food from his auburn hair and fine clothes. There was nothing left for him to do but to scuttle off back to his own land.

Now the third wedding feast was prepared but this time it was followed by a wedding night which was happy indeed. The next morning, Pwyll and Rhiannon called all the guests together. They thanked the entertainers who were there – the musicians, the jugglers, and, in particular, the storytellers. And they granted favours to all who asked, for this was the custom at the time.

Kelvin Hall

CLEVER CLOGS

Uncle Bouki's wow

Now this is a tale of market-day. And this is the way *I* tell it.

One day, Uncle Bouki went off to market.

'Now be sure to come straight back,' said Auntie Bouki. 'I don't want you wandering round, poking your nose into things that have got nothing to do with you.'

'I'll come straight back,' said Uncle Bouki.

In the market there were so many people, so much fruit heaped up on the stalls, so many vegetables spilled out on the ground. There were sounds tickling his ears and smells tickling his nose. Uncle Bouki didn't come straight back. He did wander around.

He came to an old woman with a donkey. She was sitting on the ground, resting her knobbly back against the knobbly donkey.

The donkey was eating the grass, trying to kick the old lady now and then because he didn't like her leaning against him.

And the old woman was eating... something... What could it be? It was yellow and juicy, and the way it ran down the old woman's chin and her tongue went searching after it, made Uncle Bouki feel very short of something.

'Excuse me. What's that you're eating?' he said. But she couldn't hear him above the noise of the market. 'What's that stuff you're eating?' he said again. No answer.

And at last she got fed up with his standing and staring, and suddenly shouted at him, 'Mind your own business and go away!' (She was having trouble enough dealing with the donkey.) So he went on a bit, feeling even more short of something.

At the next stall was a man. He was eating away too. Whatever it was, he was holding it in both hands, so Uncle Bouki couldn't see it. But he could tell it was crisp and juicy and sweet, from the way the man was eating it – chomping away, and sometimes stopping to pick a bit out of his teeth, then chomping away again.

Uncle Bouki just gazed. 'What's that you're eating?' he said at last. The man couldn't hear. He said nothing – just went on chomping.

Uncle Bouki coughed. 'Tell me what it's called,' he said. 'I'd like to get some for myself.'

But the man just chomped away, not hearing anything – until suddenly he got fed up with Uncle Bouki and he shouted, 'Go away and mind your own business!' So Uncle Bouki went away.

He saw an old man sitting on the bank, scooping something out of a bowl and stuffing it into his mouth with his fingers. A handful of something green. A handful of something orange. The juice dripped between his fingers and the man hummed away happily between mouthfuls.

'What's that you're eating?' said Uncle Bouki. 'Where can I get it?'

But the man didn't hear, not only because the noise of the market was too loud, but also because the man was very deaf even in the quietest places. He just scooped round the bowl, and put another handful in his mouth, something green again.

'Where can I get it? What's it called?' said Uncle Bouki again.

The old man could see Uncle Bouki's lips moving, even though he couldn't hear him saying anything, and as he was a polite and friendly man he smiled at Uncle Bouki before he took another handful.

This made Uncle Bouki think he was teasing him, and he felt even more short of something thing than ever.

'Tell me what it is!' he shouted, seizing the old man by his shirt.

Just at that moment the old man scooped something red into his mouth, and it was peppery, really peppery! 'Wow!' he shouted.

'Thank you,' said Uncle Bouki, letting go of him. 'I've never heard of that. I'll get some.'

The man said, 'Wow! Wow!' again and Uncle Bouki said, 'I heard you the first time. No need to shout.'

So the next stall he came to, he asked for some wow. But they just stared at him.

'Never heard of it.'

The next stall was the same.

'How much is wow?' he said.

'Never heard of it.'

Well, he walked from stall to stall, asking for wow. And first they stared, then they began to laugh, then they *roared* with laughter. And by now Uncle Bouki was very cross indeed, as well as hungry.

'I'll go home,' he said to himself, 'and get Auntie Bouki to cook me some.'

Now Auntie Bouki was a very fine cook, the best cook in the village. Just as he came in at the door, she had got fed up with waiting for him, and she was putting the dinner on the table.

And it was so crusty and crispy and juicy and sizzly, and the luscious smell of it curled up to Uncle Bouki's nose and tickled it so lovingly, that any other day he would have grabbed a chair and eaten it up at once.

But all the time he had been trudging home he'd been thinking 'I'll get Auntie Bouki to make wow. Wow Pie... or Wow Tart... or Wow Pudding... or Wow with sweet potatoes... or Wow with orange sauce.'

So he just grabbed the dish off the table and shouted, 'What's this rubbish! I want wow!'

And he threw it at Auntie Bouki.

At that moment, Tiji, their little boy, came in at the door. He had smelled the dinner, you see.

But just as he came in he heard Uncle Bouki's shout, and the crash of the dish, and he turned to dash out again.

'Just a minute,' shouted Uncle Bouki, grabbing him. 'Here's some money, and here's a sack. Get me some wow! Now!'

So poor Tiji went outside. What a job, to get wow! He went next door to their neighbours, but they hadn't got any. They'd never heard of it. He tried the people on the other side. Same thing. He went up and down the village, but everyone stared and shook their heads... then began to laugh... then *roared* with laughter.

Tiji sat down in the road, and wondered what to do. How could he go back without wow, with his father in that terrible temper, and dinner all over the wall?

Clever Dick came along, whistling.

'Hello Tiji.'

'Hello Clever Dick.'

'What's the matter with you today?'

And Tiji told him what was the matter.

No wow.

Clever Dick listened carefully.

'I see,' he said. 'Well, you know how it is. All troubles vanish when Clever Dick comes along. Just give me the sack and the money, and Uncle Bouki will have his wow before he knows what has happened to him. Clever Dick knows how to get it.'

He was away for not much more than five minutes... ten at the most.

When he came back he had put the prickliest leaves he could find at the bottom of the sack, and on top of them, things he had found strewn over the road after market-day – a run-over pineapple, a squashed orange, two broken yams, and one, two, three sweet potatoes that children had been kicking along for a game.

'There!' he said, handing the sack back to Tiji. 'Special delivery for Uncle Bouki.'

Tiji took it in.

Uncle Bouki grabbed it from him, untwisted the top, and almost fell inside. He pulled out the run-over pineapple.

'That's not a wow! That's a pineapple!'

He pulled out the orange.

'That's not a wow! That's an orange!'

He pulled out the yams, one, two of them.

'That's not a wow! Those are yams!'

He pulled out the sweet potatoes, one, two, three of them.

'That's not a wow! Those are potatoes!'

Tiji was beginning to feel very worried indeed. He should never have listened to Clever Dick.

But just then, Uncle Bouki plunged his hand right down to the bottom of the sack, in the middle of those prickly leaves.

'Wow! Wow!' he shouted.

And Tiji skipped out of the house. He was so pleased Uncle Bouki had got what he wanted.

Snip snap snover,

That tale's over.

Leila Berg

Bella and the bear

Bella lived in a cottage beside a dark, dense forest. One summer's day, her friends called on her to go picking berries in the woods. Before she left, her mother warned, 'Don't go too far; it's dangerous in the forest.'

Off skipped the girls towards the forest edge.

Bella knew that the biggest and juiciest berries grew in the forest glades; almost without noticing, she wandered out of sight of her friends, moving from glade to glade, filling her basket with berries – strawberries and bilberries, raspberries and cranberries, bogberries and cloudberries.

All the while she was going deeper and deeper into the forest. Suddenly, she glanced up and, to her horror, realised she was lost.

'Hell-ooooo! Hell-ooooo!' she called.

There was no reply. But someone heard her all the same: from the trees came a rustling and a cracking of twigs, and out stepped a big brown bear. When he set eyes on the little girl, he threw up his arms in joy.

'Aha,' he cried. 'You'll make a fine servant, my pretty one.'

Taking the girl roughly by the arm, he dragged her to his cottage in the depths of the dense dark wood. Once inside, he shouted at her, 'Now stoke the fire, cook some porridge, scrub the floor, make my home clean and tidy.'

Bella's life became a misery. Day after day she toiled from dawn to dusk, afraid the bear would eat her. All the while she thought of how she might escape. Finally, she had an idea.

'Mister Bear,' she said politely, 'would you take a present to my parents to show I'm alive and well?'

'Oh, all right,' growled the bear. 'I'll take it to them.'

Bella baked some cherry pies, piled them high upon a dish and fetched a big basket. Then she called the bear.

'Mister Bear, I'll put the pies in this basket. Mind you don't open the basket or touch the pies. I'll be watching you from the rooftop!'

'All right, my pretty one,' grumbled the bear. 'Just let me take a nap before I go.'

No sooner was the bear asleep than Bella quickly climbed on to the roof and made a figure out of a broomstick, her coat and headscarf. Then she scrambled down, squeezed into the basket and pulled the dish of cherry pies over her head. When the bear awoke and saw the basket ready, he lifted it on to his broad back and set off for the village.

Through the trees he ambled with his load and soon felt tired and footsore. Stopping by a tree stump to rest, he was just about to open the basket when he heard Bella's voice.

'Don't sit there all day and don't touch those pies.'

Glancing round he could just make out her figure on the roof.

'My, my, that maid has sharp eyes,' he muttered to himself.

Up he got at once and continued on his way.

On he went, carrying the heavy basket. Soon he came to another tree stump.

'I'll just take a short rest and eat a cherry pie,' he thought, puffing and panting with the weight.

Yet again Bella's muffled voice was heard.

'Don't sit down or touch those pies. Go straight to the village as I told you!'

He looked back, but could no longer see his house.

'Well, I be jiggered,' he exclaimed. 'She has eyes like a hawk, that girl.'

So on he went. Through the trees he shuffled, down into the valley, on through the groves of ash, up grassy knolls until, finally, he emerged into a meadow.

'I must rest my poor feet,' he sighed. 'And I'll just have one small pie to refresh me. Surely she cannot see me now.'

Yet from nowhere came a distant voice.

'I can see you, I can see you. Don't touch those cherry pies. Go on, go on your way.'

The bear was puzzled, even a little scared.

'What good eyes she has,' he growled, hurrying across the field.

At last he arrived at the village, stopped at Bella's door and knocked loudly.

'Open up, open up!' he cried gruffly. 'I've brought a gift from your daughter.'

The moment they heard his voice, however, all the dogs of the village came running. Their barking startled him so much, he left the basket at

the door and made off for the forest without a backward glance.

How surprised Bella's parents were when they opened the door to find the basket and no one in sight. Her father lifted up the lid, stared hard and could scarcely believe his eyes. For there beneath the cherry pies sat the little girl, alive and well.

Mother and father hugged her tight and said what a clever girl she was to trick the bear. Soon all her friends heard the news and came running to hug and kiss her too. Bella was so happy.

In the meantime, deep in the forest, the old bear reached his home and shouted to the figure on the roof to make his tea. Of course, it did not take him long to discover that the wise young girl had tricked him and escaped.

All the same, Bella never went into the forest again.

James Riordan

The farmer and the boggart

About a hundred years ago there lived a farmer called William, with Margaret his wife and three daughters, Lucy, Ruth and Grace. They weren't a wealthy family and did all the work themselves on their tiny farm.

One market day in autumn, at the nearby town, William met the neighbouring farmer whose fields joined on to his own.

'Just the man I'm looking for!' said the farmer. 'You know that small field with the brook at the bottom, next to the spinney?'

William nodded.

'Well I'm thinking of selling. It's no use to me and I wondered if you might be interested in buying it.'

William was, especially once he heard how cheap the price was. So the two of them set off for the lawyer and swiftly reached an agreement.

That evening the whole family celebrated the good news, and as the sun began to set in the west, William took his daughters down to their new field. They sat in the late autumn sun and talked of the picnics they would have by the brook next summer and of the crops they would grow.

Suddenly a shadow fell across the family, and they looked up in surprise. There towering over them, with long arms almost reaching the ground and hair all over its body and face was a terrifying creature... a boggart.

'Get off my land!' snarled the boggart.

'Your land?' asked William.

'My land!' repeated the boggart.

William, who was always very polite replied, 'I'm terribly sorry, but I think there has been some mistake. I've just bought this field this afternoon.'

'You can't have. It's mine,' snapped the boggart.

'Well perhaps you'd like to come and meet my lawyers in court,' said William.

'Court! Lawyers!' screamed the boggart who looked as if he was about to explode. He spat on the ground and muttered something which sounded as if it might be extremely rude, but which fortunately nobody could quite hear.

They waited in silence.

'I'll tell you what I'll do. I'll take half of everything that you grow.'

The daughters looked at each other and then at their father.

'I don't know,' he said slowly.

'Yes, that's fine,' interrupted Lucy. 'What do you want – tops or bottoms?

'What do you mean "tops or bottoms"?' asked the boggart.

'Above the ground or beneath the ground,' replied Lucy.

'Tops,' snapped the boggart and stumped off into the dusk.

'What are you up to, Lucy; giving away half our crops to him,' complained William.

'I think I can guess,' said Ruth.

'Me too,' said Grace. 'Why don't we plant potatoes in the spring?'

Autumn turned to winter, the trees shed their leaves and the frost fringed the brook with ice. In the spring the family planted potatoes in the field and waited as the crop began to grow. By July they had a fine field of potato plants ready for harvest.

The morning that the family went down to the field with their spades, ready to dig up the potatoes, they found the boggart waiting for them with his cart.

'I've come for my tops,' growled the boggart.

'Of course,' smiled Lucy, sweetly, 'you may have them once we've finished digging up the potatoes.'

The boggart swore horribly, for he had forgotten that potatoes grow underground and the top of the plant is quite useless.

'Next year,' he finished, 'Next year I'll have the other....'

'Bottoms?' asked Ruth.

'Yes, bottoms,' shouted the boggart and roared off into the distance pulling his cart.

The next spring, William planted wheat, and again the crop grew well, so that by the time they came to harvest it in August there was a magnificent field of wheat. Again, on the day the family went to reap the wheat with their scythes at the ready, they found the boggart waiting with his cart.

'I'm ready for my bottoms,' he cried.

'Of course,' said William. 'Just as soon as we've harvested the wheat.'

Then the boggart realised that he'd been tricked again and howled most dreadfully. But as he howled, he thought, and the beginnings of an idea came into his head.

'Next year you plant wheat again, farmer, and next year we'll both reap the crop together and keep what we each can mow.'

William looked worried. The boggart smiled a crooked, evil smile.

'See you next year,' he cackled and almost seemed to dance as he pulled his cart away.

'What on earth shall we do?' sighed William. 'He's twice as big as me, and so much stronger. He'll harvest far more than I can.'

'Don't worry, father,' said Grace, 'I think I've got the answer to your problem. Leave it to me.'

Another year passed as the field was ploughed and harrowed ready to receive the grain which settled and grew into an enormous crop of wheat. Meanwhile, Grace was persuading her friend the blacksmith to make her forty very thin iron rods which she hid in one of the barns until the night before the family was due to begin the harvest. That evening she slipped down to the field by the edge of the brook and placed the rods, two or three paces apart, upright amongst the corn.

The next morning, William took his scythe down to the field to meet the boggart. He was feeling worried and the boggart knew it.

'Good morning,' leered the boggart, 'You remember our agreement?'

'Yes, of course,' replied William as politely as ever. 'Where would you like to begin?'

'If I were you, I'd start at the top here,' said Grace. 'It's far easier going.'

A strange chortling noise came from the back of the boggart's throat, and his eyes began to water. They realised that he was laughing.

'You think you're going to trick me today as well do you? Well think again. I'm going to start down there.' And he moved off down the slope towards the brook.

Grace crossed her fingers and smiled at her father.

William and the boggart began to mow, their scythes gleaming in the sun. But whereas William kept working slowly and smoothly, every few minutes the boggart had to stop to re-sharpen his blade.

'Tough old stalks on this corn,' he muttered to himself.

Each time he had to stop, he got crosser and crosser, until finally he threw down his scythe in a rage.

'This field never was any good. You can take the field and the crops. I'm not wasting any more of my time round here.'

And without another word, or a backward glance, he walked away and was never seen again.

William lived to farm the land for many happy years, and the story he loved most was telling how his clever daughters helped him beat the boggart.

Hugh Protherough

Clever Mary and the stone soup

Now, I'm sure you've heard all about Jack before, because he's always cropping up in stories. Why, we couldn't get rid of him even if we wanted to! So you probably know from some of the stories you've read or been told that Jack isn't too clever – not too bright at all.

However, Jack had the good fortune to marry Mary and she had plenty of brains. She had enough brains for both of them put together and a few left over besides, and whenever there was any serious thinking to be done, well that was Mary's job.

Now Jack and Mary were travellers. They would travel the length and breadth of the country picking up odd jobs wherever they went and often, when they needed some food or a bed for the night, they would walk up to the nearest farmhouse, knock at the door and ask the farmer for a night's board and lodging. Then in the morning they would do a few jobs around the farm before moving on, and sometimes Jack would tell the farmer's children a story, or perhaps Mary would sing them a song with her voice as sweet as a nightingale's.

Exactly what time of year this story takes place I couldn't tell you. It could have been either spring, summer, autumn or winter – perhaps that's for you to decide – but Jack and Mary had been travelling for three days, and during that time neither of them had had so much as a scrap or morsel of food to eat. Why, you can imagine just how hungry the two of them were. Three days without any food and they were so hungry that their belly buttons were rubbing blisters on their backbones! They both realised that they couldn't go much further on empty stomachs and would need to find some food to eat before the day was out.

Just at that moment they saw in the distance there was a town. And beyond the town was a hill. And on top of the hill was a farmhouse. Not a little farmhouse, but a very large farmhouse where a very rich farmer would live.

'Why, that's ideal,' thought Jack and Mary. 'If we go to that farm we'll get a fine slap-up meal, because the farmer who lives there is bound to be so rich that only the very best food will do for him!'

So that's what they decided to do and they headed down towards the town.

As they walked along the main street, however, they saw coming towards them an old tramp-man and, my, wasn't he the raggiest old man you've ever seen! He had holes in the knees of his trousers, his boots were coming apart, the tops from the bottoms (he'd tried to mend them by wrapping Sellotape around to hold them together), his overcoat was tied around the middle by a piece of old rope and perched on his head was a battered old felt hat. As Jack and Mary approached the old man he lifted his hat and bade them 'Good day', and since Jack and Mary were polite kind of people, they wished the tramp-man all the best. He then turned round to them and said, 'Now, look. If you're going to do what I think you're going to do and walk up to the top of the hill and ask the farmer for

hospitality, let me give you a word of advice – don't even waste your time!'

'Why ever not?' said Jack. 'Surely somebody who owns such a large farm would be able to spare a bit of food for two hungry travellers.'

'Now that may be true,' said the tramp-man, 'but although he's very rich, the farmer who lives up on the hill there is the meanest, most tight-fisted man that ever walked this earth and you'll get blood from a stone before you get anything out of him.'

And with that the old man doffed his hat again and took his leave.

Well, you can imagine just how upset Jack and Mary were. Of course, they'd both been looking forward to filling their bellies up at the farmhouse and now it looked as if they would have to remain hungry.

'Now, don't you worry, Jack,' said Mary. 'That tramp has given me an idea. Remember that I have all the brains, and I think I know how to trick that farmer out of some food.'

And with that she bent down and picked up a small round stone from the road and popped it into her pocket. 'If we can't get *blood* from a stone, maybe we'll be able to get *food* from a stone!'

Soon Jack and Mary had walked up the hill and were standing outside the farmhouse. Mary knocked loudly three times on the door and waited until it swung open and standing before them was the fat, rich, greedy farmer. But even before Jack or Mary got a chance to speak, the farmer said, 'Now look, if you've come here begging for food, don't even waste your breath, because you're getting nothing from me, so be on your way!'

'Why, that's all right,' said Mary innocently. 'We've not come here begging of food. Jack and I have got our own food. All we need is a pan of water to cook it in, because tonight we're going to have some delicious, beautiful, mouth-watering stone soup!'

'Stone soup?!!' growled the farmer. 'What on earth is stone soup?'

'You mean you've never had stone soup before?' asked Mary incredulously.

'Certainly not,' said the farmer. 'I've never had stone soup before.'

Mary reached into her pocket, took out the stone she'd picked up from the road and showed it to the farmer.

'You see this stone?' she said. 'Well, this stone is no ordinary stone, for this stone is a soup stone and it was given to me by my mother and before she had it, it belonged to her mother. So it's been passed down through the generations from mother to daughter until it came to me. Now all you need to do with this stone is to pop it into a pan of boiling water and it will make the most wonderful soup in the world. Why, if you've never tasted stone soup, then you haven't lived.'

Now that farmer was fond of his food, too right he was, but he'd never had stone soup before and he could feel his taste buds tingling as he imagined the delicious stone soup that Mary had just described.

'Look,' he said, 'do you think if I were to let you have a pan of water to cook your soup in, you'd let me have a little taste of it – just to see what it's like?'

'We'll do better than that,' replied Mary. 'If you let us have a pan of water, then we'll share our stone soup with you this evening.'

The deal was made and the farmer went and fetched a pan full of water while Jack and Mary gathered some fuel and kindled a little fire. The pan was put on the fire and they waited until the water got hot and the steam was rising from the pan. Soon the water was bubbling and boiling away and Mary dropped the stone, PLOP! into the water. She took a large wooden spoon from the inside pocket of her jacket, wiped it on her shirt and gave the water a stir. She waited for a couple of minutes and then took a little taste. SLUURRPP!!

'Mmm,' she said, 'that is delicious stone soup. I think it's almost ready now. All it needs is a little pinch of salt, because all soup needs a small pinch of salt to bring out the flavour and stone soup is no different.'

'Well,' said the farmer, 'that is true enough, and I suppose if it's only salt you're wanting, I've got some salt in the kitchen and you could have some of that.'

Mary thanked him and the farmer rushed off to the kitchen for the salt.

A minute or so later the farmer reappeared carrying the salt in a small clay dish. Mary took a pinch and sprinkled it into the water. She gave it another stir with her wooden spoon and then another taste. SLUURRPP!!

'Mmm,' said Mary, 'wonderful! That is the best stone soup I've ever tasted.'

The farmer licked his lips. 'But there's still something missing,' continued Mary, and after a moment's hesitation, 'I know! An onion! Of course, you can't have stone soup, not *real* stone soup, without an onion.'

'Well,' said the farmer, 'if it's only an onion you're wanting, I've got one in the vegetable rack. I expect you could use that – if it'll make the stone soup better.'

So the farmer went back to the house to fetch the onion. Mary peeled it, chopped it and into the pan it went. She gave it another quick stir and then another quick taste. SLUURRPP!!

'Fantastic!' exclaimed Mary. 'That onion makes all the difference. All it needs now is a carrot... and maybe a potato or two, and then it will be perfect!'

Now the farmer had potatoes in the north field and carrots in the south field. Up to the north field he went for the spuds, down to the south field for the carrots, he brought them to Mary, they were scrubbed, scraped and chopped, and into the pan they went. Another quick stir and another quick taste. SLUURRPP!!

'Perfect!' announced Mary and the farmer rubbed his tummy and his mouth watered. 'All it needs now is a little bit of meat or fish – just to finish it off.'

The farmer had a little bit of chicken left over from the Sunday lunch which he had put on a plate in the fridge, so he brought it out. Mary scraped the meat from the bones and it too was added to the soup.

Now... after the meat went the parsnips. After the parsnips, the turnips. After the turnips, the swede. After the swede, the beans. After the beans, the lentils. One thing after another until soon Mary had a bubbling pan of piping hot soup.

When the soup was finally ready, Mary took the stone from the pan and placed it on the ground. She then dished out three bowlfuls of that soup; one for Jack, one for the farmer, and an extra large one just for herself.

They all licked their bowls clean and the farmer said, 'That was the most delicious soup I have ever tasted. I've never had stone soup before, but that was so good that I could eat it every day for the rest of my life. I don't suppose you'd consider selling me that soup stone, would you?'

'Well, I'm not sure,' said Mary. 'That's a very good soup stone – you've tasted the soup yourself. I'll be wanting a lot of money for a soup stone like that one.'

'I'll give you ten pounds for it,' offered the farmer.

'Oh no,' said Mary. 'I'll be wanting at least twenty pounds for this soup stone.'

'Very well,' said the farmer and he reached into his back pocket and took out his wallet. He opened his wallet and out of it brought two crisp ten pound notes, which he handed over to Mary. Mary took the money and put it quickly into her own pocket and the farmer took the stone and put it in the farmhouse kitchen. But when he came out again... well, Jack and Mary were already long gone.

Now I'm not sure what it was exactly, maybe it was just that he didn't have the knack, but that farmer was never able to make stone soup quite as well as Mary had been able to do.

Ah, now Jack and Mary were all right though. They had the money in Mary's pocket and there were plenty more soup stones where that one came from, and for all the travelling they did, they never again went without a hot meal in their bellies.

So that's the story of how Jack and Mary managed to trick the greedy farmer out of some food, and if you're ever in that position – empty stomach and empty pockets – well, maybe you'd like to try the trick yourself. But if you do, a word of advice.

Make sure you pick a rich 'un
And the best o' luck to you!

And that's a story we always call a 'Jack Tale', because it's a story with Jack in it, but who do you think is the *real* hero of this one?

Mike Dunstan

The parrot's advice

Once upon a time there was a princess who had a pet parrot, and this parrot was a remarkable bird, for it didn't simply copy what others said, it could talk and hold real conversations just like a person. The princess was very fond of this bird and had a magnificent cage built for it, made all of pure silver, and it was fed on the finest foods that a parrot could desire, and all of its needs were attended to by the princess's own servants. Every morning, before breakfast, the princess would come to visit the parrot in its cage and tell it of all the little things that were worrying her – and ask for its comments and advice. The parrot always responded thoughtfully to the princess, but secretly it thought to itself, 'Ach, how sick I am of this trivial talk, if only I could escape from here.' But although it had a great deal of time in which to think of how to do it, it never found a way.

One day the parrot heard the princess talking to one of her servants who was to accompany the king on a long journey to far off lands. She was giving him a shopping list of perfumes and silks to bring back. When the conversation was finished, the parrot whistled for the servant to come over to the cage, and then said to him, 'It so happens that you're going near that land of my birth, so will you do me a favour?'

'What is it?' asked the servant.

'If you should meet any parrots who look like me and who you think could be relatives of mine, tell them of me and where I live, and tell them how miserable I am imprisoned in this cage. All the luxuries I have and the delicacies I am fed are of no comfort or value to me for I stare at a shut door all day long.'

The servant agreed to do this. But truth to tell, he travelled for so many months with the king, and to so many exciting places, that he completely forgot about the princess's parrot, until at last, one day, as he travelled along a dusty road, he saw a large flock of parrots, just like the princess's, flying towards him. The parrots settled in a nearby tree and, remembering

his promise, the servant approached the tree and, feeling a little foolish, called his message up to the flock. To his delight, as soon as he had finished talking, one of the parrots flew down and landed on his wrist. The servant went to stroke the parrot's back, but as he did so, the parrot rolled over and lay lifeless in his hands. He jiggled the parrot's legs, but there was no response. He shook the parrot's wings, but its eyelids didn't even flutter. The bird was obviously dead. Very disappointed, and slightly disgusted, the servant threw the parrot's body towards the base of the tree, but as the bird was flung into the air, it opened its wings and soared skywards, followed by the rest of the flock. The servant was left standing by the tree feeling very bewildered.

Well, there were many more months of travelling before the servant eventually returned to the palace. A few days after his arrival, the princess's parrot called him over and asked, 'Nu[1]? Did you remember what I asked of you?'

'I did remember,' replied the servant, 'but what can I say to you? I was hoping you wouldn't ask, because the most terrible thing happened...' and he told the story.

The parrot listened with its head on one side, but made no comment, and at the end of the story nodded, as if in sympathy with the servant's surprise at the turn of events.

The next morning, the princess came to visit her parrot as usual and found it lying dead in the bottom of its cage. She screamed and she cried and she tore her hair. 'You wicked careless idiots,' she shouted at her servants, 'you have killed my bird.'

She ordered them to dispose of the body in a fitting manner, but said she was too upset to see them to do it. So the servants took the bird out of the back door of the palace, and after some discussion amongst themselves, decided to throw the body over on to the rubbish heap where the princess would certainly never see it. But as the body was flung into the air, the parrot's wings opened and it soared up into the air and flew away, never to be seen again.

Only then did the servant understand what the parrot's advice had been.

Pamela Marre

1. 'Nu?' A Yiddish expression meaning 'So?'. It is used often in conversation.

Coyote the trickster

In the very beginning the winters were bitterly cold. The men and women and children huddled together, wrapped in animal skins, beneath the stretched hides of the tepees, beneath the bitter snow and sky.

And such was the strength of those first winters that many of the old people, and many of the children, died of the cold. And so, one day, the chief of the tribe decided to set off in search of old Coyote, old grey-muzzle Coyote of a thousand tricks. He trudged through the snow-laden forests, he clambered up the icy slopes of the mountains, until he found himself standing outside Coyote's cave.

'Coyote, Coyote!'

'Coyote, Coyote!'

Out of the shadows old Coyote's grey muzzle appeared.

'Coyote, Coyote, the winter is cold, the people are dying, can you help us to find warmth in this bitter season?'

Coyote came forward and reached out with his foot, with the pad of his paw he stroked the chief's arm. He felt how there were no feathers, there was no fur, no scales, no bark. He felt pity for the terrible nakedness of the people.

'Very well, I will help you. Go back to tepees, all will be well.'

Now Coyote knew many things, and one of the things he knew was that high on one particular mountain there lived the three Fire Witches. If he could steal fire from them and give it to the people then maybe... maybe there would be warmth enough to loosen the deadly grip of the winter.

So as soon as the chief was gone, Coyote set off running, running, until he came to the foot of that mountain, and he climbed it, keeping his belly low to the ground.

He hid among the furze at the top of the mountain and watched the Fire Witches as they squatted on the ground, feeding the sacred fire. Their hair was the red and yellow of firelight, their eyes flickered like flames and their fingers were long and black and twisted as burnt sticks.

All day Coyote watched them as they crouched beside the fire, and at night he watched them take it in turns to keep guard. Two of them wrapped and wound blankets around themselves and slept in the firelight, while the third kept watch. And when the watcher grew tired, she woke up one of her sisters, and when that watcher grew tired she in turn woke up the remaining sister. And so, throughout the night the watch was shared between them.

And Coyote saw there wasn't a moment by day or by night when the fire was left unguarded... except... just before the sunrise, when the outside air is at its coldest and sleep is at its deepest. At that moment the Witch who had been watching was quick to wrap herself in the blanket and fall asleep, and the Witch who was being woken was slow to shake off the deep sleep of early morning.

Coyote saw that at that moment the fire was left unguarded. Old grey-muzzle Coyote of a thousand tricks saw, and he grinned, and he ran down the mountain. And he called together some of his friends, he called together Chipmunk, and Frog, and Robin, and Wood, and he told them his plan – and they agreed to help him.

Old Coyote waited until nightfall, and then he climbed the mountain again and hid among the furze. All night he waited, and then, just at that moment before the sunrise, when one Witch was quick to fall asleep, and another was slow to wake, he snatched a burning stick from the fire and set off, leaping and bounding down the mountainside.

The Witch who was waking opened her flickering eyes just in time to see him, the flaming stick between his teeth, disappearing over the brow of the mountain. She screeched and scratched at her sisters with her long fingers. 'Wake! There is a thief! Wake, sisters! Stop, thief!'

They shook off their blankets and screaming and pointing they hurtled down the mountain after Coyote.

Now, these Witch sisters had long, black, bony, bandy legs, and they could run at the speed of fast-spreading fire, and they began to catch up with Coyote, and one of them reached forwards and grabbed him by the tip of his tail – but Coyote was quick and threw the fire to Robin. And where the tip of Coyote's tail had been touched by the Witch's hand it turned the white of wood-ash, and to this day all coyotes have white tips to their tails.

But now Robin had the fire and the Witches were after him, he was fluttering and flying down the mountain, beating his little wings against the air, and the Witches were getting closer.

One of them reached forwards and caught Robin in the cup of her hand – but Robin was quick and threw the fire to Frog. And where Robin's breast had been cupped in the Witch's hand it turned the red of a flame, and to this day all robins have red breasts.

But now Frog had the fire, and the Witches began to catch up with him. He was leaping and leaping with all the strength of his back legs, but one of the Witches jumped forwards and grabbed him by the tail – but Frog was quick and left his tail in the Witch's hand, and threw the fire to Chipmunk. And to this day, no frogs have tails.

And now Chipmunk was scurrying down the mountain, and the Witches were catching up with him, and one of them reached forwards and with three of her long black fingers she scratched Chipmunk's back –

but Chipmunk was quick and threw the fire to Wood, and Wood swallowed the fire and stood still. And where the three fingers of the Witch had scratched Chipmunk's back, three black stripes appeared, and to this day all chipmunks have three black stripes along their backs.

But now Wood had swallowed the fire, and he stood still, and the Witches began to move in a circle around him.

'Give us the fire! Give us the fire or we'll tear your bark, break your branches, rip your leaves to ribbons!'

But Wood stood still and would not give them fire. And so they tore his bark, they broke his branches and ripped his leaves. But still Wood would not give them the fire he had swallowed.

Cursing and spitting, the Witches looked at one another, shrugged their shoulders, and returned to their mountain, to guard the sacred fire from any other thieves.

Now, Coyote had been watching everything. He had seen Wood swallow fire, and he knew that, from that moment onwards, there would always be fire inside wood. And so old grey-muzzle Coyote of a thousand tricks went down to visit the people, he went into the tepees and he showed the people how to take the fire out of wood. He showed them how, by rubbing two sticks together they could make a spark, he showed them how to feed dry moss to the spark, and dry twigs to the moss, and dry sticks to the twigs, he showed them how to make fire.

And the people never forgot, and even today we use fire to loosen the bitter grip of winter.

Hugh Lupton

The Three Spinners

Once there was a girl who was very very lazy. What she liked to do best of all was... nothing.

One day her Mother found her curled up beside the fire.

'Get a move on, girl,' she complained. 'There's work to be done, the cooking and the cleaning, chopping up firewood and fetching water. Who is doing it? I am!'

She pointed at a basket of flax waiting to be spun. 'What about this flax? It is not going to spin itself, you know.'

'I wish it would,' mumbled the girl.

'What did you say?' roared her Mother.

'I said, it will have to spin itself, because I am not going to do it. I hate spinning.'

This was just too much and her Mother gave her a stinging slap.

'Ooouuch!' shrieked the girl, and began to cry.

Just at that moment the Queen passed by in her carriage. She heard the crying and wanted to know what was wrong, so she knocked at the cottage door.

'Oh... Your Majesty,' said the Mother, curtseying. 'We were not expecting you.'

'Whaaa!' said her daughter.

'Be quiet, girl!' hissed her Mother. 'It's the Queen.'

'I hope nobody is ill?' inquired the Queen.

'Oh no, your Majesty,' said the Mother, feeling very embarrassed.

'Whaaaaaaaa!' said the girl.

'It's my daughter.'

'You didn't hit her did you?' asked the Queen.

'Well... umm... I just had to.'

And the Mother began to think very quickly indeed. 'My daughter just loves spinning you see. She would spin from morning to night if she had the chance. We only have one basket of flax and she wants to spin it all. I had to hit her, otherwise we would have nothing left.'

'Is that so?' said the Queen. 'If she loves spinning, she must come and live with me. I have three huge rooms full of flax, just waiting to be spun.'

There was nothing the Mother could do. The girl was called, and bundled into the Queen's carriage.

They arrived at the palace and she was taken up a steep spiral staircase to the three rooms. The first had flax all over the floor, and in the centre was an old spinning wheel. The second had flax piled half way up the walls. The third was so tightly packed with flax, the Queen didn't dare open the door in case it fell on top of them.

'Now, my dear, if you can spin these rooms of flax in three days, then you can marry my son.'

And the girl was left alone.

Well do you think she wanted to marry the Queen's son? Of course she did! So she set to work right away.

'Spinning can't be that difficult,' she said, as she sat down at the wheel.

Now I don't know if you have ever tried to spin, but it is not as easy as it looks. She picked up a stalk of flax; it was hard and coarse like string. She began to tap her foot on the treadle, to turn the wheel, but the wheel went round backwards. She tried to twist and pull the flax in her fingers, like she'd seen her Mother do. But it got into a terrible tangle and the dry fibres snapped. Then the flax cut into her fingers until they bled. With that she kicked the spinning wheel over and began to cry.

'Oh, I will never spin all this flax in three days.'

Then she heard a croaky old voice.

'Are you in trouble, girl?'

She looked around and couldn't see anyone.

'Do you need some help?' said the voice again.

She went over to the window and peered out. What a sight met her eyes, and it was not Rumpelstiltskin! For there stood three of the strangest old ladies she had ever seen in her life.

The first had one foot like yours or mine. But the other foot was as flat as a frying pan, and came crashing down with every step she took. The second had one top lip like yours or mine. But the bottom lip was as large as a dinner plate, and hung over her chest, swinging to and fro. The third had one thumb like yours or mine. But the other thumb was like a great, red, swollen balloon.

'What's the matter, child?' they asked.

'Well I have to spin three rooms full of flax in three days. If I do, I can marry the Queen's son. But I couldn't do it, even if I had three hundred years.'

'What a bit of luck, that you should meet us. We are the Three Spinners and we love spinning, don't we, sisters?'

The three old ladies nodded at each other.

'But you don't get something for nothing, do you sisters?'

The three old ladies shook their heads.

'What do you want in exchange?' asked the girl.

'To be invited to your wedding. We love weddings, don't we sisters?'

The three old ladies nodded.

'But you must call us your dearest Aunts and welcome us as your most important guests?'

'Is that all?' cried the girl. 'That's easy! Come in, come in.'

The Three Spinners climbed the staircase. The one with the big foot sat down at the spinning wheel, and began to tap her foot on the treadle. The wheel went round, in the right direction, so fast you couldn't see it.

The one with the big lip picked up some flax and drew it across her lip, licking it loudly. The wet flax became a neat tight strand, that couldn't cut your hand.

The one with the big thumb began to twist and pull the fibres, between her big thumb and forefinger. The flax slipped smoothly on to the bobbin, and there was a spool of finely spun thread.

The girl stood by and watched.

In a twinkling of one eye one room was done.

In the twinkling of two eyes two rooms were done.

In the twinkling of three eyes all the rooms were done.

The Three Spinners stood up. 'Remember your promise,' they said, nodding.

The girl was so happy. She had three whole days to do exactly what she liked best of all... nothing.

Then the Queen arrived. She walked slowly from room to room examining the spools of flax.

'This is marvellous... fine and strong... I have never seen anything like it... you have done an excellent job. You shall marry my son.'

The girl's heart leapt with joy.

'My dear,' said the Queen, 'with you around we shall never need to employ a spinner again.'

The girl's heart sank. What was she going to do? But she wanted to marry the Prince so much, so she said nothing.

She was taken to the Queen's chamber and introduced to the Prince. He was handsome and kind, and thought the girl was very clever. He asked for her hand in marriage rather shyly, and the girl accepted right away. She was so excited that she quite forgot about all the spinning she would have to do.

They began to plan the wedding at once. The invitations were sent out and the girl made sure she invited her three Aunts.

Then the day arrived. The rings were exchanged and the promises made and the guests were invited to a huge banquet. Everyone in the kingdom was there to see the Prince and his new bride. Everyone, except the three old ladies. The girl looked around and breathed a sigh of relief. Perhaps they were not going to come after all. Dinner was served. The bride and groom sat at the high table and all the guests sat below them.

Just then the doors burst open and in came the Three Spinners. Everyone stared in silence, their forks raised to their mouths. Then all at once they began to whisper.

'Goodness me, look at that foot.'

'The lip, my dear, have you ever seen anything like it?'

'Who invited them?'

'That thumb is disgusting.'

'Whose relations are they?'

The girl was horrified. How could she call them her dearest Aunts, in front of such important guests?

'If only the earth would open and swallow me up,' she thought to herself. But of course it didn't. Her promise was not so easy to keep after all. But she summoned all the courage and kindness she had inside her, and stood up. All eyes were upon her as she crossed the room.

'Welcome, my dearest Aunts,' she said, and a gasp went round the hall. Then she bent and kissed each one, saying, 'Come and sit with us at the high table.'

She gave the Three Spinners the most important place, in between herself and her husband. The Prince welcomed them kindly and turned to the one with the big foot, 'I am so glad you could come to our wedding.'

Then he didn't know what to say. All he could think about was the foot, 'Ummm... how did you get such a big foot?'

'By treading, my son, by treading!' she replied.

'Oh,' he said, and turned to the second old lady. 'I'm so glad you could come... how did you get such a great big lip?'

'By licking, my son, by licking.'

'Oh, I see,' he said thoughtfully and turned to the third, 'How did you get such a great big thumb?'

'By twisting, my son, by twisting.'

'OH, I SEE,' shouted the Prince, thinking about all the spinning his wife had done. He leapt to his feet and raised his glass, proclaiming in a loud voice, 'I would like it to be known that from this day forth, my beautiful wife, will never, ever, touch a spinning wheel again.'

At that everybody cheered. But the bride's cheer was the loudest of all, because she was freed from the hateful spinning wheel forever!

But perhaps she had done something far more difficult?

The three old ladies nodded.

Snip, snap, snout. My story is out!

Pomme Clayton

THE BRAVE AND THE FAITHFUL

Mister Fox and his bag

This is the story of Mister Fox and his bag and what he put into his bag and what happened to him.

Early one morning Mister Fox got up and went out hunting. He picked up his bag, put it over his shoulder and strode outside. The sun rose in the sky.

As he walked along he heard a noise. Bzzzzzzzz... it was a bumble bee. So Mister Fox grabbed the bumble bee and shoved it into his bag.

He walked and he walked till he came to a little cottage where he knocked at the door. A little old lady opened the door. He strode straight into the kitchen and plonked his bag down on the ground.

'May I leave my bag here while I go and visit my mate Morris?' he asked the little old woman.

'Of course you may,' she said.

'Very well,' said Mister Fox, 'but there is one thing. While I'm gone, MIND YOU DON'T LOOK IN MY BAG.'

'Ooh no, I wouldn't dream of it,' replied the little old woman.

But no sooner had Mister Fox gone off down the bottom of the lane, turned the corner and disappeared out of sight, than she began to grow curious. She wondered what might be inside the bag. She thought, 'I'll take one little look, it won't matter.'

So she undid the top of the bag and Bzzzzzzzzzzzzzzz, out buzzed the bumble bee.

'WHAAARGH!' cried the little old woman.

She didn't like that bumble bee at all. It flew straight past her and out into the farmyard where there was her cockadoodledoo. And it ate the bee up in one gulp.

At that moment back came Mister Fox. He wasn't daft, he could see that there was no bee in the bag.

'Here,' he said, 'where's my bee?'

'I'm sorry,' said the little old lady starting to cry, 'I only took one little look and this great big bee with a huge stinger came out and nearly stung me to death and it went into the farmyard and my cockadoodledoo gobbled it up.'

'In that case,' said Mister Fox striding into the farmyard, 'I shall take your rooster instead.'

And with that he grabbed the cockadoodledoo and shoved it into his bag.

Off went Mister Fox walking. The sun rose higher in the sky. And he walked and he walked till he came to another cottage where he knocked at the door. An old man opened the door. Mister Fox strode straight in to the kitchen and plonked his bag down on the floor.

'May I leave my bag here while I go and visit my friend Felix?' he asked.

'Of course you may,' said the little old man.

'Very well,' said Mister Fox, 'but there is one thing. While I'm gone, MIND YOU DON'T LOOK IN MY BAG.'

'Oh no, I wouldn't dream of it,' replied the old man.

So off goes Mister Fox down the lane. No sooner had he got down the bottom of the lane, turned the corner and disappeared out of sight than that old man began to grow curious. He began to wonder what was inside the bag. It kept on shifting and shuffling and making funny squawky noises. So, he thought to himself, 'I'll take just one little look. It won't matter.'

So, he undid the top of the bag and took a little look. And what does he see but a great big rooster's red eye staring back at him. 'WHAAARGH!' – he didn't like that. So he took another look. And what did he see but a great big rooster's beak. And the cockadoodledoo shot out of the bag, past the old man and into the farmyard.

In the farmyard there was a big, fat pig and it chased the cockadoodledoo round the farmyard, not once, not twice, but three times. The cockadoodledoo didn't like that, oh no, so it shot through the fence, ran over the field, and into the forest. And was never seen again.

At that moment back came Mister Fox. He strode straight into the kitchen. I've told you he wasn't daft. He could see that the bag was empty.

'Here,' he said, 'Where's my cockadoodledoo?'

'I'm sorry,' sniffed the old man. 'I only took one little look and this great big chicken came flying out with a beak like an axe blade and it nearly pecked me to death and it ran into the farmyard where my pig chased it away.'

'Right,' said Mister Fox. 'I'll take your pig instead.'

Now I've told you that the pig was fat and the pig was big. So he had some trouble getting it into the bag. In the end he put the bag over its nose and put his foot on its bottom and he pushed and pulled till he got the pig into the bag. Then off he strode down the lane without so much as a 'see you later'.

He walked and he walked and the sun rose higher in the sky. Soon he came to another house where a lady lived. He strode straight into the kitchen without even knocking and said, 'May I leave my bag here while I go and visit my cousin Clive?'

'Of course you may,' said the lady.

'Very well,' said Mister Fox, 'but there is one thing. While I'm gone, MIND YOU DON'T LOOK IN MY BAG.'

'Oh no, of course I wouldn't,' said the lady.

So off goes Mister Fox down the lane. No sooner had he got to the bottom of the lane, turned the corner and disappeared out of sight than she began to grow curious. She wondered what was inside the bag. She thought, 'I'll take just one little look, it won't matter.'

So, she undoes the top of the bag and takes a look. And what does she see but a piggy eye staring back at her, 'WHAAAARGH!' She doesn't like that. So, she takes another look what does she see? A wet piggy snout looking out at her. And the pig shot out of the bag and chased her across the kitchen. She leapt on to a chair and the pig ran into the farmyard.

There was her little boy. He picked up a stick and smacked the pig on the bottom round the farmyard. Not once, not twice, but three times round the farmyard. Now the pig didn't like this so it shot through the fence, went over the field and into the forest beyond. And it was never seen again.

At that moment back came Mister Fox. He strode straight into the kitchen. I've told you he wasn't daft and it didn't take much to see that the bag was empty.

'Here,' he said, 'where's my pig, where's my bacon, where's my pork chops, where's my running rasher?'

'I'm sorry,' said the lady, crying. 'I only took one little look and this great big pig with huge sharp teeth like knives came out and nearly bit me to death and it ran into the farmyard where my little boy chased it away.'

'Right,' said Mister Fox striding into the farmyard. 'I'll take your little boy instead.'

And with that he grabbed the little boy and tried to put him into the bag. But the boy didn't want to go into the bag – well, you wouldn't want to go into the bag, would you? So that little boy bit and he scratched and he punched and he said some terrible things but it was no good. In the end, the fox got him into the bag. He tied up the top, slung the bag over his shoulder and off he went. And as he went down the lane the, boy's mother stood at the doorway and she could just hear her son's muffled voice calling out from inside the bag.

'I may never see my boy again,' she thought.

Mister Fox walked and he walked. And as he walked the sun rose right high into the sky. He licked his lips and thought to himself. 'I feel hungry....'

But just at that moment he came to another house. He strode straight into the kitchen and dumped his bag on the ground. He looked round the kitchen and saw three girls sitting at the table waiting for their dinner, a huge dog lying sprawled in front of the oven and the girls' mum making gingerbread.

'May I leave my bag here while I go and visit my niece Nancy?' asked Mister Fox.

'Of course you may,' replied the girls' mum.

'Very well,' said Mister Fox, 'but there is one thing. While I'm gone MIND YOU DON'T LOOK INSIDE THE BAG.'

'Oh no, we wouldn't dream of it.'

So off went Mister Fox walking, walking. No sooner had he got down the bottom of the lane, turned the corner and disappeared out of sight than the mother put the gingerbread into the oven. Oh it smelt so good, even Mister Fox who was three miles away by now could smell it. It made his belly rumble. Soon those girls were calling, 'Mum, Mum, I want a slice of gingerbead,' and 'Mum, gimme a bit please....'

And the little boy in the bag could smell the gingerbread too, so he calls out, 'Gimme a slice of gingerbread.'

WHAAAARGH!' screamed the girls. 'Mum, that bag spoke!'

They'd never had a talking bag in their house before and they were curious. So they crept over and untied the top. There was the boy, of course. Now you should know that their mum was clever. So she took the boy and hid him in the broom cupboard. But she knew that if they left the bag empty then Mister Fox would know that they had hidden the boy. So they had to put something else into the bag instead. So what do you think they put in instead? No, the gingerbread was too small. What else was in the kitchen? The dog! Yes, they put the big dog into the bag and tied up the top.

At that very moment in strode Mister Fox. He looked round the room and smelled the gingerbead. Hmmmm, his tummy rumbled. How hungry he felt. He picked up his bag and it felt the right weight so off he went without even a 'thanks' or a 'by your leave'.

And he walked and he walked with the sun at its highest in the sky. He thought, 'I'll go down to the stream and have a drink and then I'll have a nice tasty bite to eat.'

So, down he went to the stream where he drank. SLUUURP. Then he untied the top of the bag and out jumped the dog and it ate him up in three big gulps. GRUFFF, GRUFFF, GRUFFF.

Then the dog had a drink and lay down for a bit. Later that afternoon the dog walked home and the girls had saved him some gingerbread. But he said, 'No thanks, I'm too full of fox.'

The next day, the dog walked the boy back to his home and when his Mum saw him come walking up the lane she ran down to meet him. There was such a kissing and a cuddling that I can't begin to tell you about it.

Now, that is the end of my story of Mister Fox and his bag and what he put into it and what happened to him.

Pie Corbett

Piñoncita

There was once a little girl called Piñoncita[1]. Her mother loved her, her father loved her, but there was one thing strange about her. When she was born, she was very very small and she never got any bigger. And she was small. Very small. Very, very small.

So tiny was she that her mother and her father had to make everything specially for her – special clothes, special bowl, special bed, special sheets.

The little girl's father was often away, tending sheep on the mountains. And because she was so very tiny, her mother was always worrying about her. Maybe someone might step on her by accident. Maybe she would get lost. So always her mother warned her, 'You must not go out of the house on your own.'

One day, the mother was dashing out to the market to fetch something she needed for dinner. Before she went, she said the same thing as usual: 'You must not go out of the house on your own.'

But what did Piñoncita do?

Of course, she went outside, out into the garden at the back of the house. How she got there I cannot tell you – whether it was under the door or out through the keyhole. All I know is that when she got there, it was magical. The flowers were as big as trees; the garden was like a forest. She ran about enjoying it all – until it began to rain! The drops of rain were enormous.

'Ouch!' she shouted as they landed on her head.

Where could she go for shelter? The rain was making puddles and the puddles soon came up to her knees.

'Help!' she thought. 'What shall I do? If I don't find somewhere to hide, I might drown.'

Then she saw a mushroom. 'I know,' she thought, 'I'll climb up the mushroom. It can be like an umbrella for me.'

Quickly she climbed up the stalk of the mushroom and held on tight to the brown frills underneath. But soon she heard footsteps and a big loud voice.

'Here's a nice mushroom,' the loud voice said.

And suddenly, a hand was picking her umbrella and – Whomp! she was inside a basket with lots of other mushrooms about her. Then she was swinging about in the basket as the mushroom-picker carried it home.

1. Pronounced 'Pin-yon-see-ta'

Piñoncita called out, 'Help! Help!'

But no one heard because she was inside the basket.

Soon she was in a kitchen and tipped into a pan of water, still holding on to the mushroom. Next, the mushrooms were swished about, lifted up and lowered into a saucepan full of hot stew. Piñoncita didn't like it. It was very very hot.

'Help, help,' she called.

But no one heard because she was inside the saucepan.

She decided to sing a song that she knew. Perhaps it would cheer her up. She didn't know where it came from but she liked it just the same:

Kwm-by-ya-a-a. Kwm-by-kwe-kwo. Kwm-by-ya-a-a.

Kwm-by-ya-a-a. Kwm-by-kwe-kwo. Kwm-by-ya-a-a.

Suddenly, a spoon came down into the pan. Piñoncita thought good, it would save her. Instead it lifted her out, still clinging on to her mushroom, and sailed her through the air and she ended up in a great big mouth. It was dark in the mouth, and there were big white teeth.

'Help, help,' called Piñoncita. But no-one heard so she sang her song:

Kwm-by-ya-a-a. Kwm-by-kwe-kwo. Kwm-by-ya-a-a.

Kwm-by-ya-a-a. Kwm-by-kwe-kwo. Kwm-by-ya-a-a.

The song sparked off an idea. 'I know,' she thought. 'If I bite the lip, maybe the mouth will spit me out.'

So she bit the lip and the mouth spat her out – right across the kitchen to the grass outside the front door.

'Phew!' said Piñoncita!

Unfortunately for her, just as she sat up a hungry donkey came along. Clip, clop, clip, clop. The donkey was looking for nice things to eat and when it saw Piñoncita, still clinging on to the mushroom, it thought here was some nice juicy food. It licked her up and swallowed her down – and Piñoncita swam down its throat and ended up in its stomach. It was dark in there – and squelchy – and smelly.

'Help! Help!' she called.

But no one heard because she was inside a donkey.

She sang her song to cheer herself up:

Kwm-by-ya-a-a. Kwm-by-kwe-kwo. Kwm-by-ya-a-a.

Kwm-by-ya-a-a. Kwm-by-kwe-kwo. Kwm-by-ya-a-a.

It gave her a brilliant idea. 'If I tickle the inside of this donkey's tummy, maybe it will feel funny and spit me out.'

So she tickled and tickled and tickled and tickled and the donkey felt funny indeed. It coughed and spat and coughed again and out came Piñoncita.

Piñoncita was now in a bit of a mess. She rolled over on the grass to clean herself up. Over she rolled and over and over. To a bird flying past, high up in the sky, she looked like a fat juicy worm. 'Just right,' thought the bird, 'for my baby birds in the nest.'

The mother bird flew down. She picked up the thing that looked like a worm and, holding it in her beak, flew back into the sky.

'Help! Help!' called Piñoncita, just as she had before.

This time, someone heard.

'Good gracious,' said the bird. 'What was that voice?'

'It was me,' called Piñoncita crossly. 'I'm not a worm. I'm a little girl.'

'Oh dear,' said the bird. 'You'd better come to my nest. You can live with me and my babies.'

So the mother bird brought Piñoncita to a nest high up in a tree. Inside were several baby birds, all squeaking and squealing for food. The mother bird flew away to fetch worms. But while she was gone. Piñoncita heard a loud hissing and, looking up, she saw a snake looking over the edge of the nest.

'Oh dear,' thought Piñoncita. 'I must do something to frighten it off or it will kill the baby birds.'

Quickly, while she thought, she sang her song:

Kwm-by-ya-a-a. Kwm-by-kwe-kwo. Kwm-by-ya-a-a.

Suddenly, she remembered the safety pin her mother had put in her trousers because although her mother had made them specially small, they were still a bit too big and they needed the pin to hold them up. As soon as Piñoncita thought about it, she undid the pin and held it out and flashed it in the air like a sword.

'Sssssss,' said the snake and slithered quickly away.

Just then, the mother bird came back.

'I can't thank you enough,' she told Piñoncita. 'I saw you protecting my babies. You're a very brave little girl and I'd like to do something to thank you. What reward would you like?'

Piñoncita did not have to think long before she knew exactly.

'I'd like to go home,' she said.

'That's easy,' the mother bird replied. 'Climb on to my back and I'll take you.'

When Piñoncita was sitting on her back, the mother bird lifted her wings and flew away, over the fields, over the rivers, over the hills and far away until Piñoncita saw her house down below.

'There's my house,' she called to the bird.

The mother bird flew down to the ground and set her down in a field near the house.

'Before you go home,' she told Piñoncita, 'I want you to look for a bone. When you find it, take it home. I think it will bring you good luck.'

The bird flew away. Piñoncita looked around. Soon she saw a bone. She couldn't have missed it, it was so big. Very big. Very, very big. So big she couldn't possibly carry it because she herself was so very small. She wondered what to do.

'I know,' she thought. 'I'll sing my song.'

Kwm-by-ya-a-a. Kwm-by-kwe-kwo. Kwm-by-ya-a-a.
Kwm-by-ya-a-a. Kwm-by-kwe-kwo. Kwm-by-ya-a-a.

The song made her think what to do with the bone. Putting her hands against it, she tried with all her strength to push it. She heaved. It rolled. She pushed again. Again it rolled, over and over. And each time it rolled, she noticed something strange – the bone was getting smaller and she was getting bigger. She rolled it again. The same thing happened. The bone got smaller and she got bigger until by the time she reached her house she was the size of an ordinary girl and she could pick up the bone in her hand.

Piñoncita knocked on the door and her mum opened it. Her mum gave her a big hug. Then Piñoncita told her mother the story of her adventures. Can you remember all that had happened?

Mary Medlicott

Kakarat

Once there was a poor widow who had four children, three girls and a boy. The first girl's name was Lilee-Lilee. The second girl's name was Filambo. The third one's name was Filam-Batam and the boy was called Kakarat.

Now, there's something I think you ought to know about these children. The girls were beautiful, as lovely as can be, but they were not very nice, I'm afraid. You see, they were as vain as they were lazy and idle. They spent hours and hours preening themselves, plaiting their hair in fancy styles and worst of all, they were very unkind to Kakarat their brother. Whenever visitors came round they would push him to one side and say to him, 'Hide your face, you ugly boy.'

Kakarat, on the other hand, was a very sensible boy. He would help with all the chores round the house. He'd polish the windows till they shone. He'd scrub the wooden floor until it was so clean you could eat off it. He'd sweep the yard and help his mum in the garden growing yams and sweet potatoes. In his spare time he'd wander through the woods and make friends with the animals.

Every Friday morning, the widow used to go to the village market to sell her fruit and vegetables. With the money she made, she'd buy clothes, food and lovely treats for her children, especially her three girls. Every Friday morning before leaving for the market, the mother would warn her children, saying, 'Don't open the door to anyone while I'm away. When I get back you'll know it's me because I'll sing this little song.'

And she'd sing:
Lilee-Lilee come here
Filambo come here
Filam-Batam come here
But Kakarat stay there.
With that she'd lift her basket to her head and set off for the market.

One Friday morning, bright and early, mum got up as usual to prepare her basket for market. Kakarat got up to help her and together they put in yams, sweet potatoes, pineapples, some juicy avocado pears just ready for eating and, just before lifting her basket to her head, she reminded the children as she always did.

'Don't open the door to anyone when I'm gone. When I return, you'll hear my song and only then must you open.'

The song as you know went like this:

Lilee-Lilee come here
Filambo come here
Filam-Batam come here
But Kakarat stay there.

As soon as she'd finished her song, the widow went off to the market, heavy basket firmly perched on her head.

Now this is where the story really begins. That morning, hiding near the house behind a cluster of bushes was a very sinister looking character. He was half human, half monster, with long hairy arms, nails like claws and rolling red eyes. His name was Zokla. Now Zokla had a very bad reputation in the neighbourhood as a child-snatcher. Whenever a child disappeared from one of the villages people would say straight away, 'Hm... Zokla take him!' or 'Zokla take her.'

This Zokla had been listening with great interest to the conversation between the widow and her children. He had memorised every word of the song. He rubbed his hands in glee, waited a long while to make sure mum had really gone, then he crept up to the house.

Zokla took a deep breath and in a gravelly and really awful voice he sang:

Lilee-Lilee come here
Filambo come here
Filam-Batam come here
But Kakarat stay there.

The children heard this dreadful singing and had a jolly good laugh.

'That's not mum's voice,' they laughed. 'It's too awful.'

So of course, they didn't open the door.

Zokla thought to himself, 'I've got to do something about this voice of mine.'

So he trotted across to the blacksmith's forge. A blacksmith, as you know, is someone who works with iron and makes shoes for horses. This blacksmith was busy working away, melting and shaping iron. He had a roaring fire on which sat a pot of boiling, steaming water.

'Oi, let's have a cup of hot water,' shouted Zokla gruffly to the blacksmith.

'Why you want a cup of hot water?' the blacksmith asked.

'Never you mind, just gimme!' said Zokla rudely.

To tell you the truth, the blacksmith was a little afraid of Zokla, so he gave him a cup of hot water without any more argument. Zokla took the cup of hot water, then he fetched some herbs, squashed and crushed them into the hot water till it turned green and slimy. He then drank the hot potion in a few great gulps and pulled a terrible face. It tasted disgusting. But Zokla didn't really mind for those were no ordinary herbs. They had the power to change the most atrocious voice into something soft and gentle to listen to. Zokla waited for the potion to take effect and then he tested his voice to see whether the herbs had worked. Noisily he began to test his voice: 'Aah! Err! Ooh! Oweee!'

The last note was perfect. Zokla hurried back to the house and this time with a voice as gentle as a lark's he sang:

Lilee-Lilee come here
Filambo come here
Filam-Batam come here
But Kakarat say there.

The children heard Zokla's song.

'Mum's back,' the girls said, about to rush to the door, but Kakarat held them back.

'This isn't mum. She can't be back so soon. Don't open the door.'

But when had the sisters ever taken any notice of Kakarat? They simply pushed him aside and went to open the door. Well, alas, standing at the door was not mum but this half human, half monster with long hairy arms, nails like claws and terrible rolling red eyes. In his hand he held a sack.

He grabbed the first girl, Lilee-Lilee. Into the sack she went.

He grabbed the second girl, Filambo. 'Help! Help!' but she too went in.

The third girl, Filam-Batam, put up a struggle, 'Let-go-of-me-you-horrible...' but in the sack she went with her sisters.

Zokla flung the sack over his shoulders and with the girls wriggling and jiggling inside he disappeared into the woods. Kakarat in the meantime remained hidden and trembling under the sofa.

Some time later the widow arrived home. She'd done very well at the market. She'd managed to sell all her fruit and vegetables and had brought back coconut buns and all sorts of goodies, especially for her three girls. She put down her basket and called to
the children in their special code.

Lilee-Lilee come here
Filambo come here
Filam-Batam come here
But Kakarat stay there.

She got no response from the children. She thought perhaps they had dropped off to sleep, so she sang the song again a little louder:

Lilee-Lilee come here
Filambo come here
Filam-Batam come here
But Kakarat stay there.

Trip, trip, trip, she heard Kakarat's footsteps coming towards the door. The door opened and a very tearful and distressed Kakarat stood there.

'Oh mum, oh mum,' he cried. 'While you were gone...' and he told her the

whole story of Zokla the half man, half monster who had taken his sisters away.

Naturally the widow was very upset. She hugged Kakarat to comfort him and wept for her daughters.

'My beautiful girls, my poor, poor girls,' she cried.

Then she hugged Kakarat some more, dried his tears and told him not to worry for there must be a way to get the girls back.

Kakarat was so pleased with all this newly found attention from his mum, that he suddenly felt very brave.

'I'll go mum,' he offered. 'I'll go and fetch my sisters back.'

'Please don't go, you're all I've got left, Kakarat.'

But Kakarat was determined. 'Don't worry, mum, I'll bring them back, I promise,' he said.

So she packed him some food in a haversack and let him go.

Kakarat set off to find his sisters and at every village he'd stop and ask the same question: 'Have you seen a great big half man, half monster, with long hairy arms, nails like claws and rolling red eyes?'

To his question the villagers would always shake their heads and answer, 'No, we never see no such creature.'

At last Kakarat felt very hot, tired and hungry. He stopped near a clear stream, cooled his face, hands and feet, had a long drink and ate some of his food. Now well refreshed, he continued on his way but didn't have much luck tracing Zokla and his sisters. By now it was getting late. A round moon was just beginning to peep out from behind a hill. The sun dipped slowly down into the crimson horizon and a few stars had already come out to play.

Kakarat was on the verge of turning back but he tried one last time in this village: 'Have you seen a great big half man, half monster, with long hairy arms...?'

There was a gasp of horror from a few of the villagers. Even before he had finished describing the creature, someone said, 'Dat's Zokla you talking about! Boy, what you want with Zokla?'

Someone else, an elderly woman, took her pipe out of her mouth, spat loudly on the ground and said with some authority, 'Well if the boy have business wit Zokla, let him go an fine him Zokla. You see dat likkle house on top de hill, wit de smoke comin' out de roof? Well, dat's Zokla house, but if I was you, bwoy... I'd run home to me mooma.'

Kakarat thanked the villagers and went up and up the hill and indeed he could see Zokla's broken down little shack surrounded by thick undergrowth. Kakarat hid behind a large tree and put his thinking cap on. 'How on earth was he to get his sisters out of Zokla's clutches?'

You may remember that Kakarat had always been great friends with animals, something for which he was now very grateful, for out of the blue appeared a pair of brightly coloured hummingbirds, humming furiously on their wings. 'We'll help you.'

A pair of shimmering snakes just as mysteriously slithered up. 'We'll help you.'

Agoutis, manicous, Jacquot parrots, wild dogs, wild cats, animals large and small, all gathered round, all offering to help Kakarat.

The rooster of the bright red comb took things in hand. Drawing himself to his full height, he said to the other animals, 'When I count Wan, Two,

Tree, you all shout, you hear?'

He counted to three and, as instructed, the animals howled and hissed, mooed and meowed, they cooed and cackled, they shrieked and they stamped. From his house Zokla heard the terrific, tumultuous, thundering noise and thought a million monsters were out to get him. So he opened his door and ran and ran and ran. The animals followed in hot pursuit. What a noise they made as they chased Zokla down the hill!

Kakarat thanked and waved at his animal friends before going into Zokla's house to rescue his sisters. He found them tied to the legs of a rickety old table. Quickly he untied their wrists and ankles and together they ran and ran and ran, and never stopped until they were safely home again.

Well you can imagine the excitement and the scene of joy at their return. There were hugs and kisses all round. Mum was so relieved to see her children again. You'll be pleased to know that the girls, Lilee-Lilee, Filambo and Filam-Batam, had learned their lesson. They stopped being so vain and idle and helped around with the chores as they should have done in the first place. They had also come to love and respect their brother Kakarat. But as for Zokla, no one knows what's become of him. For all we know he may still be running. So if you ever take it into your head to go wandering off by yourself into a nearby wood, let me warn you, you might just come face to face with this half human, half monster, with long hairy arms, nails like claws and rolling red eyes. Watch out, it will most probably be Zokla and I don't want him to get you.

Messiers Crick[1]!!!

Jane Grell

The wooden trough

My father's father came from a small village in the Ukraine in Russia and was orphaned when he was very young. He came to England as a young man at the turn of the century and it was here that he met the woman who became his wife, whose family also came from the Ukraine. They had six children: large families were important in those times of course because the children, when they grew up, would eventually look after the parents. This was particularly important to my grandfather in view of his childhood and so he used to tell his children this story to emphasise how important parents are.

After my grandfather was orphaned, at about the age of seven, he was taken in by a carpenter who had an unusually small household for those days. The carpenter lived with his elderly father, his wife and one child, a son, who was only a baby when my grandfather went to live there. The carpenter took in my grandfather to help around the house with all the old jobs and to look after and provide companionship for the little boy. Indeed, when the little boy started to go to school at the age of five, my grandfather had almost total care of him and had to carry him on his back to and from school so that the child's feet would never have to touch the snow.

1. 'Messiers crick!' is a traditional Dominican storyteller's ending to a tale.

Now, as I said, the carpenter's father was elderly. He had trouble getting about the house because his hips and legs didn't work very well, his eyes watered all the time, he was hard of hearing and his hands trembled, but he was a very proud man. He had been strong in his youth and very independent and found his own frailties very difficult to accept, so he was always trying to be of use around the house. He would try to help move boxes of fruit and vegetables around the kitchen, but they were really too heavy for him to lift and his physical weaknesses made him very clumsy as well so that he would tip them up and apples and potatoes and onions would go rolling all over the floor, and then the carpenter's wife would get impatient and shout at him to go and sit down somewhere out of the way. Then the carpenter would come home from work and the old man would ask how the business was going, because he wanted to be involved, but he didn't hear half the replies because of his deafness, and would put forward irrelevant ideas or tell interminable stories that everyone had heard before, so that the carpenter and his wife grew increasingly impatient with him and tried to ignore him as much as possible, and the old man grew rather sad. The only one who didn't notice all his infirmities was his little grandson, who adored his grandfather, who always had time for him, and would sit at his feet for hours listening to any stories that his grandfather would care to tell.

Now everyone in the household would sit down together to eat the main meal of supper, and the old man, because of his hand tremor, began to spill quite a lot of his food. It would dribble down his shirt and on to his trousers, so the carpenter's wife gave him a bib to wear at mealtimes, which hurt the old man's pride dreadfully, though he didn't say anything. But then his tremor grew gradually worse and the food would splatter on to the tablecloth round his plate and drip over the edge of the table, so that the cloth looked horrible and needed changing and washing after every meal. And this began to irritate the carpenter's wife, because, after all, there were no washing machines in those days and a tablecloth was a big item to deal with. The worsening tremor also meant that as he ate, the old man could not raise his spoon or fork from the bowl or plate without hitting it, and so all through mealtimes there was the tap, tap, tap, of his shaky spoon against the crockery, which irritated the carpenter no end.

At last the carpenter's wife had an idea. She decided to lay the old man a little table of his own in the corner of the dining room, next to the stove, and she sat with her back to him so that she didn't have to watch him spilling the food on the table and himself, and the tablecloth was smaller and so easier to wash, and anyway, she didn't feel the need to change it so often because she wasn't the one who had to sit and look at it and eat from it. And that was all right for a while, though there was still the tap, tap, tap, of the spoon or fork against the crockery that irritated them all no end. But then, one day, the old man, as tactfully as he could, drew his daughter-in-law's attention to the fact that she'd forgotten to change his tablecloth for a while and it had really got rather offensive to look at. So the carpenter's wife removed it and then realised that actually, life would be much easier if the old man didn't have a cloth at all, so she never replaced it, and the old man now ate off a bare table. But he didn't complain as everyone else seemed happier, though there was still the tap, tap, tap, of the spoon or fork against the crockery that irritated the carpenter no end. So one day the carpenter had an idea. 'Look,' he said to his wife, 'the old man hasn't many teeth left and he can't manage the big pieces of food anyway because he can't chew, so why don't you boil up his food into a gruel and put into a bowl and give it to him with bread so that he can sop the bread into the bowl and that will put an end to the awful noise he makes.'

And so this is what his wife did.

Well, the old man grew sadder and quieter, but there was no point in protesting, and there was one compensation to his being separate at supper time, and that was that his grandson, who always finished his meal long before everyone else, would come and sit at his feet as the old man supped, and play and chatter away, regardless of whether his grandfather heard what he was saying or not. And so supper time became a special time for them both that they always spent together.

Well, this continued for some time until one day, the old man had become so tremulous that he knocked his soup bowl off the table and it fell to the floor and shattered, so that there was soup all over the floor mixed with a hundred tiny pieces of china, and the carpenter's wife scolded the old man for the loss of her bowl. So the next day, the carpenter went into his workshop and got one of his men to knock up a wooden trough which he brought home and gave to his father to eat out of so that there would be no more breakages. The old man grew sadder than ever, for he felt even more helpless than his little grandson, but how could he protest? At least his son was giving him a home.

Well, one day, the carpenter brought home a bag of offcuts of wood from the workshop for his son to play with. And the boy was very excited by these new building bricks that were all different shapes and sizes. So, when he had finished his meal that night, the little boy brought the bag of bricks over to the feet of his grandfather, and the two of them built houses and towers and castles until the little boy became very involved in trying to fit four similar-sized pieces together with a roof on top. But because the pieces were uneven, the structure kept falling down and the little boy eventually threw a tantrum because they wouldn't stay together.

'They won't stay, they won't stay,' cried the boy in floods of tears. 'I want them to stay together.'

'All right, all right,' said the grandfather. 'Calm down, perhaps your father can glue them for you tomorrow.'

'Yes, yes,' called his father from the table, 'I'll glue them tomorrow.'

'Why is it so important anyway? What are you making?' asked the old man.

And the little boy turned his tear-stained face to his grandfather and said, 'I'm making a wooden trough for mummy and daddy to eat out of when they grow old.'

Then the carpenter and his wife looked at each other across the supper table and their eyes filled with tears.

And from that day forward, so my grandfather told his children, the old man ate at the table with the rest of the family again, and the carpenter's wife never complained about the mess on the tablecloth and the carpenter never expressed any irritation at the tap, tap, tap, of the spoon or fork against the bowl.

Pamela Marre

The black dog

The Clan Chief of the island of Colonsay was hunting one day in the wildest, most remote corner of this wildest and most remote of the Western Islands. He came to a hut and he could not be sure whether he had ever seen that hut there before. But he went inside and there was an old man. He might have been a hunter or he might have been a shepherd, you couldn't quite tell what he was.

The old man had a bitch there who had recently given birth to a litter of puppies, and the puppies rolled and tumbled and waddled and pounced. And the best of all at rolling, tumbling, waddling and pouncing was the black one. The Chief took a strong fancy to him.

'It's come into my mind,' he said, 'that I should like to have that black puppy.'

'Any of these puppies you can have,' said the old man, 'but not the black one.'

The Chief looked into the old man's eyes and the old man looked into the Chief's eyes.

'The black one,' said the Chief, 'is the one that I must have....'

'Well if you are fixed on it,' said the old man, 'then you are fixed on it. But this I will tell you. That black dog will only ever do one day's work for you. But that day's work will be a good one!'

So it was that the little black puppy padded off with the Clan Chief of the island of Colonsay. And that puppy grew large, beautiful, powerful, hungry and completely useless. For he utterly refused to do a single day's hunting.

'That dog's no good!' the Chief's men would say. 'You should get rid of it.'

But the Clan Chief would always answer, 'No, for the black dog's day has not yet come.'

One time it was decided that they should all go on a hunting trip to the island of Jura. The morning was bright and clear. The Chief's men waited with all their dogs in the boat by the sea shore.

'Black Dog,' called out the Chief, 'come!'

But the dog just hugged the ground with its belly, with its paws out before, and would not move an inch. Even when the Chief made as if to hit it, it would not move an inch.

'That dog,' called out his men, 'is not worth the food you give it!'

But the Chief answered, 'The Black Dog's day is not yet come!'

Just after that, a great wind arose and the hunting trip had to be called off. The next morning was calm and sunny and the boat was prepared again. All the Chief's men and their dogs waited in the boat.

'Black Dog, come!' called out the Chief, but once more the dog just hugged the ground with its belly and would not budge.

'That dog,' called the Chief's men, 'is useless. You should kill it now.'

'No!' answered the Chief, 'for the Black Dog's day has not yet come!'

Immediately afterwards, a great storm blew up, and the hunting trip had to be called off.

'The dog knew a storm was coming!' the men said. 'That is why he didn't want to get in the boat. He has foreknowledge – he knows what's going to happen.'

'The only foreknowledge my dog has,' said the Clan Chief, 'is that his day has not yet come.'

Now the next day also dawned bright and clear, and once more the Chief's men waited in the boat. But that time the Chief did not even bother to try to call his dog. He just climbed into the boat and it was pushed off from the shore. At that moment the Black Dog jumped up, ran down the beach and leapt into the boat!

'Ah!' said the Chief, 'the Black Dog's day is near.'

Sixteen was the number of the men of the Clan Chief of the island of Colonsay that went with him on the hunting trip to the island of Jura. And when that night they slept in a cave, and in that cave they were attacked by demons and goblins with hideous faces – if they had faces at all – with fangs and claws razor sharp, then the number of the men that died was sixteen. But when those demons and goblins came to the place where the body of the Chief lay, still asleep, they found him protected by a huge, ferocious black dog that would not let one of them pass.

So fierce was that dog that he drove every one of them away. By that time the Chief was awake and standing with his sword in his hand. But as he did so, through a crack high up in the wall of the cave there slithered a long arm, with at its end, a claw. And this came down from the wall of the cave and across the floor towards the Chief's ankle. But just as it reached him, the black dog turned around and sprang, and clamped its jaws around the wrist of that claw. He did not let go until the claw lay, severed from its arm, on the floor of the cave. The arm slithered back through the crack, and the dog ran out of the cave to deal with whatever monster owned that arm.

After a time he trotted back into the cave, came up to the Chief, jumped up on his hind legs, and put his paws on the Chief's shoulders and licked his face. Then he went back down on his four legs and keeled over and died. For he had done the one day's work for which he had come into the world.

So the Clan Chief of the island of Colonsay was the only living thing to return from the hunting trip to the island of Jura. After this happened, a saying spread among the people of the Western Isles. It was in their Gaelic language, but it translates into English as 'The Black Dog's day is yet to come.' The saying then spread far and wide, and we use it when we say, 'Every dog has his day.' And of course, that saying is not just about dogs.

Kelvin Hall

Little Semyon

There was once a poor man who lived with his three sons in a small house beside a vast swamp. Now this swamp was so big that it took three years to go around it. The man thought to himself, 'This is no good that it takes so long to go around the swamp. My sons and I will build a fine white hazelwood bridge across it.'

So the man and his sons built a bridge across the swamp. It took them a long time but when it was done, the swamp could be crossed in three days instead of three years. And when the bridge was built, the man said to his eldest son, 'Ivan, my beloved son, go and hide yourself beside the bridge and see what men say of our work, whether it be good or evil.'

So Ivan went and hid himself under the bridge, and soon two old hermits came and stood on the bridge and said, 'To whoever built this bridge, the Lord will grant whatsoever he may wish.'

Then Ivan jumped up and said, 'I built this bridge, together with my father and my brothers.'

'Then say what it is that you want,' said the hermits.

'I wish that I may be rich for the rest of my life,' answered Ivan.

'Go and dig under the roots of the old oak tree,' said the hermits. 'There you will find treasure, enough to make you rich for the rest of your life.'

And Ivan went and dug under the roots of the old oak tree, and there he found treasure, enough to make him rich for the rest of his life.

The next day the man said to his second son, 'Demetri, my beloved son, go and hide yourself beside the bridge and see what men say of our work, whether it be good or evil.'

So Demetri went and hid himself under the bridge and soon the hermits came and stood on the bridge and said, 'To whoever built this bridge, the Lord will grant whatsoever he may wish.'

Then Demetri jumped up and said, 'I built this bridge, together with my father and my brothers.'

'Then say what it is that you want,' said the hermits.

'I wish that I may have bread for the rest of my life,' said Demetri.

'Then go and plough the field behind the tree and plant it with grain and you shall have bread for the rest of your life,' answered the hermits.

So Demetri went and ploughed the field behind the tree and planted it with grain and he had bread for the rest of his life.

On the next day, the man turned to his youngest son and said, 'Little Semyon, Little Semyon, my beloved son, go and hide yourself beside the bridge and see what men say of our work, whether it be good or evil.'

Little Semyon went and hid under the bridge and soon the hermits came and stood on the bridge and said, 'To whoever built this bridge, the Lord will grant him whatsoever he wants.'

Then Little Semyon jumped up from under the bridge and said, 'I built this bridge, together with my father and my brothers.'

'Then say what it is that you want,' said the hermits.

'I wish that I may be a soldier in the Great King's army,' replied Little Semyon.

'Little Semyon, Little Semyon,' said the hermits, 'you are young and foolish and a soldier's life is hard. Think again.'

'No,' said Little Semyon. 'That is what I want.'

The hermits touched Little Semyon and he turned into a stag, and as the stag he ran to his father's house, but his father and brothers didn't recognise him and tried to shoot him. He ran back to the hermits and they touched him again and he turned into a hare, and as the hare he ran to the house but his father and brothers tried to shoot him. He ran back to the hermits and they touched him again and he turned into a little bird with a golden head, and as the bird he flew to the house, but again they tried to shoot him and he flew back to the hermits and they touched him one more time and he regained his own form.

'Go now with our blessing,' said the hermits, 'and be a soldier in the Great King's army. But if ever you need to travel fast, you can change yourself into any of these animals. We have shown you how.'

Little Semyon went back to the house and said good-bye to his father and brothers and then he set off for the palace. When he got there he went to see the Great King and asked to be a soldier. But the Great King said, 'Little Semyon, Little Semyon, you are young and foolish and a soldier's life is hard.'

'I may be young and foolish,' said Little Semyon, 'but I will serve you as well as any man.'

And the Great King made him a soldier and kept him close about him.

Now it happened that shortly after, a king from a far distant land declared war on the Great King. To protect his land, the Great King summoned his army and set out to meet the enemy and he took Little Semyon along with him.

For three years the Great King and his army marched, until they came near the enemy and battle was to be joined in three days. But then the Great King realised that he had left his sharp sword and battle mace behind in the palace.

He called his army together and said, 'I have left my sharp sword and battle mace behind in the palace and without them we shall be defeated. If any of you can bring them to me in three days, to him I will give half of my kingdom and my daughter, the Princess Maria, in marriage.'

Well, some said they could make the journey and back in three years, some in two, some even in one. But Little Semyon stepped forward and said, 'Do not worry, your Majesty. I will fetch your sharp sword and battle mace and bring them to you in three days.'

The Great King wrote a letter to his daughter, the Princess Maria, telling her to trust this messenger and to give him his sharp sword and battle mace. Little Semyon took the letter and walked out of sight of the king and his army, then he changed himself into the stag, and as the stag he ran and ran and ran until he was exhausted. Then he changed himself into the hare, and as the hare he ran and ran and ran until he was exhausted. Then he changed himself into the little bird with the golden head, and as the bird he flew and flew and flew until, in a day and a half, he reached the palace.

He stopped outside the palace and changed himself back into his own form. Then he went in and found the Princess Maria and gave her the letter. When she had read it she asked how he had managed to make the journey so quickly.

'Like this,' he said and he changed himself into the stag, and as the stag he ran once around the room and came and put his head on the princess's shoulder. She took out a pair of scissors and cut a tuft of hair off his head and wrapped it in her handkerchief. Then he turned himself into the hare, and as the hare he ran once around the room and jumped up into her lap and she cut off a tuft of fur and put it in her handkerchief. Then he changed into the little bird with the golden head and flew once around the room and landed on her shoulder. She plucked a single feather out of his head and put that in her handkerchief too.

Little Semyon took back his own form and the princess kissed him and gave him her father's sharp sword and battle mace. He went outside and turned himself into the stag, and as the stag he ran and ran and ran until

he was exhausted. He turned himself into the hare, and as the hare he ran and ran and ran until he was exhausted. Then he turned himself into the little bird with the golden head, and as the bird he flew and flew and flew, until he came in sight of the Great King and his army.

He stopped out of sight and took on his own form, then started to walk towards the Great King and his army. But as he was walking he began to feel very tired and he thought that he would just have a rest before going to the Great King. He lay down on the sea shore and, in the blink of an eye, fell fast asleep.

But it happened that a wicked general from the Great King's army was walking along the shore and he saw Little Semyon lying there with the sharp sword and battle mace beside him.

'Ahhhh,' thought the general. 'If I kill Little Semyon and take the Great King his sharp sword and battle mace, then I will marry the Princess Maria and inherit half of the kingdom.'

He picked up the sleeping Little Semyon and threw him into the sea and when he did so, the Sea King rose up out of the water, took ahold of Little Semyon and pulled him under the waves.

The wicked general took the Great King his sharp sword and battle mace, and with it he defeated his enemy. Then the Great King and his army set out for their own lands, a journey of three years.

Little Semyon lived a year in the palace of the Sea King and when a year was over he began to weep and weep and weep.

The Sea King said to him, 'Little Semyon, Little Semyon, are you so sad here with us? Do you wish to return to your own land?'

'Yes,' said Little Semyon. 'Yes, I do.'

And at midnight, the Sea King placed Little Semyon on the sea shore and Little Semyon prayed and prayed and prayed that the sun might touch him. But before it could, the Sea King rose up out of the water, took ahold of him and carried him under the waves.

And when a year was past, Little Semyon began to weep and weep and weep, and the Sea King said to him, 'Little Semyon, Little Semyon, are you so sad here with us? Do you wish to return to your own land?

'Yes,' said Little Semyon. 'Yes, I do.'

And at midnight, the Sea King placed Little Semyon on the sea shore and Little Semyon prayed and prayed and prayed that the sun might touch him. But before it could, the Sea King rose out of the waves, took ahold of him and carried him back to his palace.

And when another year had past, Little Semyon began to weep and weep, and the Sea King said to him, 'Little Semyon, Little Semyon, are you so sad here with us? Do you wish to return to your own land?'

'Yes,' said Little Semyon. 'Yes, I do.'

And at midnight, the Sea King placed Little Semyon on the sea shore and Little Semyon prayed and prayed and prayed that the sun would touch him and just before the Sea King came for him, the sun rose and shone on him.

Now he was free from the Sea King, and he turned himself into the stag and as the stag he ran and ran and ran until he was exhausted. He turned himself into the hare and as the hare he ran and ran and ran until he was exhausted. He turned himself into the little bird with the golden head and flew and flew and flew, until he reached the palace. Then he turned back into himself and went in.

The Great King and his army had just arrived home and on one side of him sat the Princess Maria and on the other side the wicked general, who had thrown Little Semyon into the sea.

When Princess Maria saw Little Semyon, she turned to the King and said, 'Hear me, O my father. It was not your general who brought you your sharp sword and battle mace in three days, but Little Semyon who stands before you.'

'Can you prove this?' asked the King.

'Yes,' they said. 'Yes, we can!'

And Little Semyon changed into the stag and ran once around the room and put his head on the princess's shoulder. She undid the first knot in her handkerchief, took out the stag's hair that she had cut off and placed it on his head. Then he changed himself into the hare and ran once around the room, jumped into her lap and she undid the second knot, took out the fur and placed it on his head. Then he turned into the little bird with the golden head, flew once around the room and landed on her hand. She undid the last knot in her handkerchief, took out the feather and placed it on his head.

The King had the wicked general banished from the kingdom and Little Semyon and Princess Maria got married and lived happily ever after.

Tim Bowley

The Old Witch

Once upon a time there lived two children, a boy whose name was Adam, and a girl whose name was Alice. Now, they lived with their old father, who was too old to work, so there was no money coming into the house, so they were poor indeed.

So, one day, Alice, who was the older of the two, set off to find work as a servant girl, and she tried every house in town, but there was no work to be had. And so she set off into the country, asking here and there, until the fields opened out into wild moorland and the trees grew thick and dark about her. She came to one last farmhouse and knocked at the door.

'Excuse me, Ma'am, would you have any work for a servant girl?'

And the farmer's wife said, 'No. And don't you go no further along that road neither, for that's the road that leads to the cottage of the Old Witch.'

But poor Alice was so tired that she was only half paying attention, and she carried on walking along that road, footsore and her eyes brimful with tears. And she hadn't gone far when she saw, standing beside the road, an old brick oven, and from inside it came the muffled voice of the bread.

'Little girl, little girl, take us out, take us out. Seven years have we been baking and no one has come to take us out.'

Well, Alice had a kind heart, and so she opened the oven door and took out the bread, steaming in its baking trays, and she set it down on the cool grass, and then she carried on along the road, footsore and her eyes brimful with tears.

She hadn't gone much further when she met a cow, and the cow called out to her in its deep voice.

'Little girl, little girl, milk me, milk me. Seven years have I been waiting and no one has come to milk me.'

Well, Alice had a kind heart, and so she milked the cow. Buckets and buckets she filled with milk, and then she carried on along the road, footsore and her eyes brimful with tears.

She hadn't gone much further when she met an apple tree, its branches heavy with fruit, and it called out to her in its whispering voice.

'Little girl, little girl, pick my fruit, pick my fruit. Seven years have I been waiting and no one has come to pick my fruit.'

And so, because she had a kind heart, Alice picked the apples from the tree and laid them on the grass beneath the branches, and she carried on along the road, footsore and her eyes brimful with tears.

And she hadn't gone much further along the road when she saw an old cottage, with a black cat, thin as a shadow, rubbing itself against the gateposts. Alice knocked at the door, rat-tat-tat, and slowly it cr-r-re-e-eaked open, and there was the Old Witch herself. Her nose bent down and her chin curled up, and between nose and chin her iron teeth clicked and clacked like knives and forks, her two red eyes peered out from under drooping lids, and her tall black hat scraped against the lintel of the doorway as she hobbled out to meet Alice.

'Excuse me, Ma'am, would you have any work for a servant girl?'

'Plenty of work, plenty of work, come inside, my pretty.'

And the Old Witch led Alice into her cottage, and she showed her how she must rub and scrub, clean until it gleamed, brush and broom every

nook and cranny and corner of the cottage, all day and every day for one little penny a month's wages. And this seemed better than no work at all, so Alice agreed to work for the Witch.

'And there's one thing more,' said the Old Witch. 'You must never, never look up the chimney. If ever you look up the chimney, terrible, terrible things will happen to you.'

So Alice agreed never to look up the chimney, and the next day she started work. She rubbed and scrubbed and cleaned every nook and cranny and corner of the cottage until it gleamed like a new pin. And all the time she was working, the Old Witch was watching her with her two red eyes, and all the time she was working, the thin black cat was watching her with its two green eyes.

And at the end of the first month Alice was given one little penny, which she put safe into the pocket of her apron.

And at the end of the second month she was given another.

And at the end of the third another.

And at the end of the fourth another.

But then one day, during the fifth month, the Old Witch went out into the woods to search for herbs for her spells and potions, and she left the thin black cat to do the watching. And while she was away, Alice was brushing the ashes in the fireplace when, just for one moment without really thinking, just for the tiniest moment with one eye only, she looked up the chimney and... THWACK!... down fell a bag of gold into the ashes, and the thin black cat ran to tell the tale to the Old Witch. And Alice, thinking that this wasn't so terrible at all, looked up the chimney again and THWACK! THWACK! THWACK! THWACK!... there were five bags of gold lying in the ashes.

Quick as a flash she heaved the bags of gold over her shoulders and set off at a run out of the cottage and along the road towards the town. But just as she was drawing near to the apple tree she heard the sound of the Old Witch's broomstick rushing through the air close behind her.

And so she called out to the tree:

Tree, tree, hide me,
So the Old Witch won't find me,
If she does she'll break my bones
And bury me under the marble stones.

'Quick, hide among my branches, hide among my branches,' whispered the apple tree.

And no sooner was Alice crouching safe among the branches than the Old Witch arrived, sitting astride her broomstick, with the black cat perched at the end.

Tree of mine, tree of mine, have you seen a girl,
With a widdy widdy wag and a long tailed bag,
Who stole my money, all I had?

And the apple tree replied in its rippling, whispering voice, 'That way, mother, that way, mother.' And pointed one of its branches down the wrong road.

And WHOOOOOSH!... off went the Old Witch along the wrong road. And no sooner gone than Alice climbed down from the tree and carried on along the road towards the town, but just as she was drawing close to the cow she heard the Witch behind her again, and so she called out to the cow:

Cow, cow, hide me,
So the Old Witch won't find me,
If she does she'll break my bones
And bury me under the marble
stones.

'Quick, quick, hide beneath the hay in my manger,' said the cow.

And no sooner was Alice safe beneath the hay than the Old Witch arrived, sitting astride her broomstick with the thin black cat perched at the end.

Cow of mine, cow of mine, have
you seen a girl,
With a widdy widdy wag and a
long tailed bag,
Who stole my money, all I had?

And the cow replied in its deep lowing voice, 'That way, mother, that way, mother.' And pointed one of its hooves down the wrong road.

And WHOOOOOSH!... off went the Old Witch down the wrong road. And no sooner gone than Alice climbed down from the manger and carried on along the road towards the town, but just as she was drawing close to the old brick oven, she heard the Witch once more.

Bread, bread, hide me,
So the Old Witch won't find me,
If she does she'll break my bones
And bury me under the marble stones.

'Quick, hide behind the oven, hide behind the oven,' said the bread.

And no sooner was Alice safe behind the oven than the Old Witch arrived.

Bread of mine, bread of mine, have you seen a girl,
With a widdy widdy wag and a long tailed bag
Who stole my money, all I had?

And the bread replied in its muffled, moundy voice, 'She's inside the oven, mother, she's inside the oven.'

So the Old Witch opened the oven door and crawled inside, thinking to find Alice hiding in the darkest corner of it. But Alice ran round from behind, and with a click she closed the oven door.

And there was the Old Witch, trapped inside the oven, scratching and scraping with her long black fingernails. And there was Alice, safe outside the oven, and off she went home with a skip in her step and a tune between her teeth.

And now there was gold enough for food, there was gold enough for clothes, there was gold to mend the hole in the roof, and there was gold and gold and gold besides. And Alice and Adam and their old father lived happy for many months.

And I wish that was the end of the story... but it isn't. Because you see, as the time rolled on, Adam began to grow jealous of Alice. He began to wish that the gold was his. He began to wish that it was he himself who had taken the gold from the Old Witch.

And so, one day, he set off in the same direction, taking first this road and then that road, until the fields opened out into wild moorland and the trees grew thick and dark about him. And soon he found himself on the road to the Witch's house, and there was the old brick oven, and from inside it the voice of the bread.

'Little boy, little boy, take us out, take us out. Seven years have we been baking and no one has come to take us out.'

'I'm in a hurry,' said Adam, and without slackening his pace he carried on along the road.

And there was the cow.

'Little boy, little boy, milk me, milk me. Seven years have I been waiting and no-one has come to milk me.'

'I've got to get to the Witch's house,' said Adam, and without slackening his pace he carried on along the road.

And there was the apple tree.

'Little boy, little boy, pick my fruit, pick my fruit. Seven years have I been waiting and no one has come to pick my fruit.'

But Adam's head was so full of the thought of the gold that he didn't even answer the apple tree.

And soon he came to the old cottage, with the black cat, thin as a shadow, perched on the gatepost, and it was rat-tat-tat on the door, and cr-r-re-e-e-eak!... there was the Old Witch again.

'Excuse me, Ma'am, would you have any work for a servant boy?'

'Plenty of work, plenty of work, come inside, my handsome.'

And Adam was led into the cottage and shown how to rub and scrub, and clean until it gleamed, and brush and broom every nook and cranny and corner of the cottage, all day and every day for one little penny a month's wages.

And he was told he must never, ever look up the chimney.

And at the end of the first month he was given one penny.

And at the end of the second he was given another.

And at the end of the third, another.

And at the end of the fourth, another.

And then one day, during the fifth month, the Old Witch went out into the woods to search for herbs for her spells and potions, leaving the thin black cat to do the watching.

And no sooner was she out of the door than Adam ran across the room and peered up the chimney and THWACK! THWACK! THWACK! THWACK! THWACK! THWACK!... there were six bags of gold lying in the ashes.

Quick as a flash he heaved them over his shoulders, and he set off running, out of the cottage and along the road towards the town.

But just as he drew near to the apple tree he heard the sound of the witch's broomstick rushing through the air close behind him, and so he called out:

Tree, tree, hide me,
So the Old Witch won't find me,
If she does she'll break my bones

And bury me under the marble stones.

But the apple tree just rustled its leaves as though it had heard no more than the wind, and so poor Adam had to carry on running along the road towards the town.

And soon the Old Witch arrived at the tree, sitting astride her broomstick with the black cat perched at the end.

Tree of mine, tree of mine, have you seen a boy,
With a widdy widdy wag and a long tailed bag,
Who stole my money, all I had?

And the apple tree answered in its rippling, whispering voice, 'That way mother, that way mother.' And pointed one of its branches down the right road.

And WHOOOOOSH!... off went the Old Witch down the right road, and soon she caught up with Adam, and she swooped down and grabbed him by the hair, and she shook him to the north, and she shook him to the south, and she shook him to the east, and she shook him to the west, and if she beat him once with the butt of the broomstick, she must have beaten him a hundred times. And when every piece of gold and every hard-earned penny was scattered across the ground, she gathered them up and WHOOOOOSH!... she was gone.

And it was black and blue and without a penny to his name that poor Adam trudged homewards.

He was butted by the old cow.

And he was burnt by the old brick oven.

But when he got home, his sister Alice, who had a kind heart, welcomed him, and rubbed ointment into his bruises, and piled his plate with food.

And with Alice's gold they lived happily for many years.

But Adam's gold was nothing but a memory, and nobody ever got far on one of those!

Bee bo bendit
My tale's ended
If you don't like it
Go to Wales
Get copper nails
And mend it.

Hugh Lupton

The seven ravens

Once upon a time, a long time ago, before you were born, before your great great great... grandmother was born, there lived a mother and a father who had seven sons. Although they loved them very much, they dearly wanted a daughter. They wished and hoped and prayed, and at last God granted them a baby girl. But she was not like you or I, she was very very tiny. She could fit into the palm of your hand and was as light as a feather.

The father was worried that she might die. So he called his sons and said, 'My sons, fetch me some water from the well. We must christen your sister as soon as we can, so that she might live.'

The boys grabbed a bucket from the kitchen, and ran helter-skelter to the well. But when they got there a terrible fight broke out. They all wanted to be the one to pull the water up from the well. They argued and they shouted.

'I am the oldest. I want to do it.'

'But I am the strongest.'

'I want to be the one to save our sister.'

'I am the youngest, let me.'

They pulled the bucket this way and that, until somehow the bucket just fell down the well. The boys were left staring over the edge of the well, into the darkness.

'What are we going to do now?' they cried.

Back at home the father was pacing up and down with his tiny daughter in his arms.

'Where are my boys? I send them out to do a job and do they do it? They have forgotten all about it. They are probably playing some game. Oh my sons are useless, they might as well be seven ravens, for all I care.'

Then he heard a whirring of wings and a cawing sound. He looked out of the window and there were seven ravens, with black wings and navy blue beaks, circling above his head.

'Caw, caw, caw!' they cried.

'Wife, come quick,' shouted the father. 'I have turned our sons into ravens.'

The mother began to cry.

'Husband, don't you know that you should never make a wish without meaning it? I just hope our daughter lives.'

The birds flew away.

The girl did live, and she grew up tall and fine and strong. But she never knew that she had brothers.

Until one day, when she was about thirteen, her mother sent her to the market. She went from stall to stall, buying bread and eggs, honey and cheese, milk and apples, when two old ladies saw her and whispered, 'You see that girl there... she's very pretty, isn't she? But do you know, her brothers were turned into ravens and flew away!'

The girl overheard every single word. She could hardly believe her ears, and ran home as fast as she could.

She burst in through the front door shouting, 'Mum, Dad, is it true that I've got brothers?'

Her mother and father sat her down and told her the whole story, about the water, the well and the terrible wish.

Then she said to herself, 'I will find my brothers and set them free, even if I have to go to the end of the world.'

That night she crept into her parents' bedroom. Beside her mother lay a golden ring, with her mother's name engraved upon it. She slipped it on to her finger. Beside her father lay a little silver penknife. She attached it to her belt. She crept downstairs and put some bread into one pocket and a bottle of water into the other. She tied a stool on to her back, in case she needed to sit down, then she set off through the forest.

It was dark and she could hear the bats flapping through the trees, the owls hooting, the wolves howling in the distance and the snakes rustling through the grass. She walked all night. She walked without stopping. She walked so far, that she came to the end of the world.

The sun stretched out its rays to burn her to a crisp. She turned and she ran, and she ran, and she ran from that place. She ran all day. She ran without stopping, She ran so far, she came to the other end of the world.

The moon was just rising and it was very very cold. The moon stretched out its beams to freeze her to an icicle. She turned and she ran, and she ran, and she ran from that place, until she came to the centre of the world.

By this time she was feeling rather hungry. So she took off the stool, sat down and ate the bread and drank the water. She looked about her and saw that the sky was full of stars. Each star was sitting on its own little stool, just like her.

Then the brightest star of all, the morning star, rose up in the sky and spoke, 'Child, your brothers are inside the glass mountain. Take this key, look after it carefully, and you can set them free.'

He bent down and gave her a little chicken bone. She thanked him and wrapped it up in her handkerchief, and went on her way.

She saw something shining in the distance. It was a mountain made of glass rising up like a sheet of ice. At the bottom was a tiny wooden door.

'At last,' she said, 'I can free my brothers.'

She opened the handkerchief, but it was empty. The chicken bone had gone. How was she going to get inside the mountain now? She needed a bone. Then she remembered that she had one. She took the silver penknife from her belt, and put out her own little finger. With one quick movement, she cut it off. She put it into the keyhole. It fitted perfectly, just like a key, and the door clicked open.

Inside there was a little man with a long grey beard.

'What do you want?' he asked.

'I am looking for my brothers, the seven ravens.'

'My masters are not at home at the moment, but you can come in and wait if you like.'

She watched him put out seven bowls and seven cups. He filled each bowl with grain and each cup with sweet red wine. The girl was so hungry that from each bowl she bit a bite, and from each cup she sipped a sup. Then into the last cup she let slip her mother's golden ring.

Then there was a whirring of wings and a cawing sound and the little man ran around shouting, 'My masters are coming home, my masters are coming home.'

She just had time to hide behind a sack, when in flew the ravens, swooping down low, stretching out their wings. Each raven knew that somebody had been eating from his bowl and drinking from his cup. They cried:

Caw, caw, well I ween,
Mortal lips have this way been.

Then they pecked and they drank, and they pecked and they drank. Until the last raven got to the last drop of wine, when he saw something glinting in his cup. He pulled out the ring.

'Brothers, look, this is our mother's ring, it has her name on it.'

All the ravens gathered round and looked.

'Caw, I wish we could see our sister again,' they said.

'If we knew she was alive, we would be free from this magic spell.'

Of course, the sister had heard every word. She stepped out from behind the sack and smiled at them.

At once all their feathers began to fall to the ground like leaves. Their beaks fell away and their claws disappeared. Standing before her were her seven brothers, whole and hale as ever they had been before. She ran up and hugged each one.

'But what is this, sister?' asked the brothers. 'You have lost your little finger.'

'Oh that!' said the girl. 'I would rather have seven brothers than one little finger.'

Then they set off for home. When they arrived there was such a party. And if they haven't drunk their fill, they must be sitting and drinking and revelling still.

Pomme Clayton

The White Bear King

Once upon a time, way up in the snowy mountains of the north, there lived a King and a Queen, who had three daughters. The King loved them all very much, but the youngest one was so sweet and pretty and funny, that he loved her a little bit more. Whatever she wanted, he gave it to her.

One night she dreamed of a golden ring, decorated with a garland of leaves and flowers. She felt that if she did not have it. she would die. Her father said, 'Of course you shall have the ring.'

So a ring was made just like the one in her dream, but when she put it on, it was too big. Another was made and it was too small. Another was made and the flowers were not right. The Princess began to feel poorly, and did nothing but lie on a couch all day. The doctor said she must eat nourishing soup, and go for a walk. Every day the Princess ate her soup and took her walk. But all she thought about was the ring.

One day she came to a part of the forest she had never been in before. There among the trees, was a huge white bear. He had a crown on his head, and in his paws he held the golden ring.

'That's my ring!' cried the Princess.

'No, it is mine,' growled the Bear.

'Well, how much do you want for it? I am a princess, and I can give you anything you want.'

'It's not to be had for money,' replied the Bear.

'What do you want for it then?' she asked.

'You may only wear this ring, if you will be my wife.'

'Marry a bear!' laughed the Princess.

But the ring sparkled so brightly, she stretched out her hand and said, 'Very well, I will marry you.'

The Bear put the ring on her finger and it fitted perfectly.

'I will come for you on Thursday,' he said.

The Princess ran back to the palace. She felt quite different. She had roses in her cheeks and her eyes shone.

'Father, look what I've got!' she cried, and told him the whole story.

'Impossible!' said the King. 'No daughter of mine will marry a bear.'

Thursday came, and the King ordered the whole army out on to the battlements of the castle. The Bear lumbered over the drawbridge, and the air filled with the whistle of arrows. But the arrows just bounced off the Bear's back, and he entered the palace unharmed. The King was sitting on his throne, with his three daughters hiding behind it.

'I have come for she who promised me her hand in marriage,' growled the Bear.

The King thought to himself, 'A bear would never know the difference.'

From behind the throne he pulled out his eldest daughter. 'Here she is, I hope you are happy together.'

And he sat her up on the back of the Bear.

The Bear charged off with her, far, far, and farther than far, until they were deep in the forest. Then the Bear said, 'Have you ever sat softer, have you ever seen clearer?'

'Oh yes!' sneered the eldest daughter. 'On my mother's lap I sat much softer, and in my father's court I saw far clearer.'

'Well you're not the right one then,' roared the Bear.

He tossed her off his back and chased her, screaming, all the way home.

'I will be back next Thursday for the true bride,' he called.

Thursday came, and the army had their cannons loaded. The Bear charged towards the castle and there was an enormous explosion. But when the smoke cleared, his fur wasn't even marked.

'I have come for she who promised me her hand in marriage,' demanded the Bear.

The King pulled out his second daughter, and sat her up on the back of the Bear.

The Bear charged off with her, far, far, and farther than far. Then he said, 'Have you ever sat softer, have you ever seen clearer?'

'Ugggh!' said the second daughter nastily. 'My mother's lap is much softer and my father's court is far clearer.'

'Well you're not the right one then,' roared the Bear, and chased her all the way home.

'I'll be back next Thursday for the true bride.'

Thursday came, and the King stood on the drawbridge alone. The Bear charged towards him, his huge mouth open, his sharp teeth shining. The King's knees began to knock, and he called to his youngest daughter.

'Here she is,' he said trembling. 'Take great care of her, for she is my dearest.'

And he sat her up on the back of the Bear.

The Bear charged off with her, far, far and farther than far. Then he said, 'Have you ever sat softer, have you ever seen clearer?'

'No never,' she whispered. 'No never.'

The bear took her to his palace.

'Everything here is yours,' he said.

That night she slept in the bed and he lay by the fire.

In the middle of the night she was woken by a ripping, and a tearing sound. The Bear was digging his claws into his fur, and tearing off his skin. Underneath there was a man. It was too dark for the Princess to see his face and before dawn he had climbed back into his bear skin. During the day he was a bear and at night he was a man.

In the first year she gave birth to a child, but as soon as it was born, the Bear took it away. She looked for it and listened for it, but she never saw it again. The next year she had a second child, and the Bear took that away. In the third year, when her third child was taken, she felt as if her heart would break. So she begged to go and see her mother and father. The Bear agreed, saying, 'You must promise that you will not do what your mother tells you to do, and you will listen to what your father says.'

The Princess set off through the snowy forest. She was given a warm welcome at the palace. The King and Queen took her to one side and asked her how it was, being married to a bear.

'During the day he is a bear, but at night he takes off his skin and becomes a man,' explained the Princess. 'I have had three children, but he has taken them all away.'

'How terrible and cruel,' said her mother. 'He must be some kind of man-eating monster. Does he have red eyes or serpent's fangs?'

'It is always too dark to see his face, Mother.'

'Well, girl, you must take this little stub of candle and look at him. Then you will see what kind of beast you are married to.'

But her father shook his head and said, 'That would only do more harm than good.'

But whether it would or it wouldn't, she took the candle and put it in her pocket.

She arrived back at the Bear's palace. When she was sure that he was asleep, she lit the candle and held it over his face. He was not a monster at all. He was very very handsome. She held her breath, gazing at him in wonder, leaning closer and closer. When suddenly, a drop of wax fell from the candle and splashed on to his forehead. He woke up with a start.

'What have you done?' he cried. 'Why couldn't you trust me? If only you had waited one more week. I would have been freed from the spell and been wholly a man. But now I must go and marry the troll hag who put the spell upon me, and be wholly a bear.'

He pulled on his bear skin.

'Can't I come with you?' begged the Princess.

'No, you have spoiled everything.'

The Bear jumped out of the window. She just had time to fling herself on his back, and cling on to his fur. They sped through the trees like the  wind, the Bear almost flying across the snow. She clung on to his back, until her hands were as cold as ice. Then she slid to the ground below. When she got up the Bear had gone, and fresh snow had fallen completely covering his tracks.

She walked through the forest all day. Just as the sun was setting, she came upon a little cottage. Outside an old woman was tending a fire. She had a long nose, a very long nose, so long she was raking the fire with it!

'Have you seen the White Bear King?' asked the Princess.

'He rushed by here yesterday. You won't catch up with him tonight. Come in and rest with us.'

Inside the cottage there was a little girl playing with a pair of golden scissors, clipping and snipping in the air. Wherever she cut, strips of silk and velvet and lace appeared like a snow flurry. The little girl said, 'Granny, this lady needs the scissors more than I do. Can she have them?'

'Of course,' said the old woman.

So the Princess put them in her pocket.

She walked through the forest all day, and just as the sun was setting she came to a second cottage. There was an old woman with an even longer nose. It was so long, she was digging holes and planting seeds in the snow with it!

'Have you seen the White Bear King?' asked the Princess.

'He rushed by three days ago. You won't catch up with him tonight. Come in and rest with us.'

Inside was a little girl playing with a golden goblet. She tipped and poured and all kinds of drinks appeared.

'Granny,' said the girl, 'this lady needs this goblet more than I do. Can she have it?'

'Of course,' said the old woman.

So the Princess put it in her pocket.

She walked through the forest all day, and just as the sun was setting, she came to a third cottage. There was an old woman with an even longer nose! It was so long, she was pulling up a bucket of water from the well with it!

'Have you seen the White Bear King?' asked the Princess.

'He rushed by a week ago. You won't catch up with him tonight. Come in and rest with us.'

Inside was a little girl playing with a white cloth. She laid it out and said, 'Cloth, spread thyself with every good dish.'

Suddenly the cloth was covered with food. They all sat down for supper.

'Granny,' said the little girl, 'this lady needs the cloth more than I do. Can she have it?'

'Of course,' said the old woman.

So the Princess put it in her pocket.

She walked until she came to a mountain made of glass, so high you couldn't see the top, and so wide you couldn't see round it. At the bottom was a hut. Inside a mother was surrounded by ragged children, pulling at her apron strings, and crying, 'Mummy, I want something to eat... I'm hungry.'

The mother filled a saucepan with stones, put it on the fire and said, 'Hush, my children, the potatoes will soon be done.'

The children stopped crying and sat down to wait for the food. The Princess was shocked.

'How can you do that?' she asked.

'It deadens their hunger, and I have some quiet,' replied the mother.

Well what would you do? You would do what the Princess did. She put her hand in her pocket and pulled the cloth out and said, 'Cloth, spread thyself and deck thyself with every good dish.'

It was covered with food. Roast meat and steaming potatoes, hot cakes and custard! The children had never seen such a feast. They ate and they ate and they ate. And then they were thirsty. So the Princess pulled out the golden goblet. Soon they were drinking hot chocolate and lemonade, and the mother had a little nip of whisky. Then the Princess pulled out the scissors and began snipping and cutting. Dresses and shirts, trousers and capes, stockings and shoes, went flying about the room.

'How can I ever thank you?' said the mother.

'I am looking for the White Bear King. Have you seen him?' asked the Princess.

'He rushed up the mountain three weeks ago. You will never get up there; not even the birds can fly to the top.'

At that the Princess began to cry.

'Don't cry,' said the mother. 'My husband is a blacksmith. When he gets home he could make you some claws like the bear's. Then you could try to climb the mountain.'

The blacksmith spent all night in his forge hammering and he made two pairs of sharp pointed claws with strong leather straps.

The next day, the Princess buckled the claws on to both hands and knees and set off up the glass mountain, digging the claws into the glass and dragging herself up, until the hut below was just a tiny speck. Digging the claws in and dragging herself up, until her body ached, and her knees were red raw. Digging the claws in and dragging herself up, until she was surrounded by swirling clouds. Digging the claws in and dragging herself up, until she was so tired she felt she could not lift her arm up again.

When she reached the top, there was a dark castle and lots of little trolls running around. They had red eyes, fat noses, hairy bellies and hairy feet.

'Have you seen the White Bear King?' asked the Princess.

'Oh yes, he's marrying our mistress,' they chanted. 'But nobody is allowed to see him except our mistress!'

The Princess walked to the gate of the castle, but it was locked. She just had to get inside. She pulled the golden goblet out of her pocket and began to pour sweet, sparkling, bubbly champagne. The gate creaked open and there was the Troll Hag. She had bony legs and a bony body. She carried her head under her arm. It had red eyes, iron teeth and wiggling rats' tails for hair. Sticks and twigs stuck out of her neck.

'OOOOOOOOHHH! Champagne!' shrieked the Troll Hag. 'Just what we need for the wedding. How much does that goblet cost?'

'It's not to be had for money. It is only to be had if I can spend a night with the White Bear King,' replied the Princess.

'Very well, but I must lull him to sleep first,' said the Troll Hag as she snatched the goblet.

That night the Princess was shown into the White Bear's room. He was in his man's form, fast asleep. She rushed to kiss him, but he did not open his eyes. She shook him, she spoke to him, but he did not wake up all night.

The next morning she sat by the gate and pulled the cloth out of her pocket.

'Cloth, spread thyself and deck thyself with a wedding cake.'

There was a huge wedding cake with three tiers and white icing. On the top was a little statue of the Troll Hag, with her head under her arm!

'OOOHHH! A wedding cake!' cried the Troll Hag. 'Just what we need. How much is that cloth?'

'It is not to be had for money. It is only to be had for a night with the White Bear King.'

'Very well, but I must lull him to sleep,' said the Troll Hag as she snatched up the cloth.

But the King was fast asleep again. The Princess stamped and shouted, begged and pleaded. But he did not hear her.

But the troll guarding the White Bear's door heard everything, and said to his master the next day, 'Sir, a young girl was here last night, weeping and crying about how much she loved you. She was awfully sweet and pretty, sir. If I were you, sir, I wouldn't drink the red wine that Mistress gives you at supper, it's drugged.'

The Princess sat by the gate and pulled the scissors out of her pocket. She clipped and snipped the most fabulous wedding dress. It had ribbons and flounces, and a special extra neck on one side, for the Troll Hag's head!

'OOOHHH! A wedding dress,' screamed the Troll Hag. 'It would fit me perfectly. Just what we need. How much are those scissors?'

'They are not to be had for money. They are only to be had for a night with the White Bear King.'

'Very well, but I must lull him to sleep,' said the Troll Hag as she snatched up the scissors.

That night the White Bear King had supper with the Troll Hag. He was in his man's form, and he carefully tied a sponge under his chin. Instead of drinking the drugged wine, he let it trickle into the sponge. The Troll Hag was so busy feeding herself, she didn't even notice. Then the King pretended to fall asleep, and the servants carried him to his room, snoring.

But the Troll Hag scowled, 'I don't trust him just one inch, bring me my sewing basket.'

She took out her longest, sharpest darning needle. 'Let's see if you are really asleep.'

She stuck the needle into the King's arm. She pushed it through the skin, through the flesh, to the bone. He did not even flinch. The Troll Hag pushed the needle through the marrow and out the other side.

'Let the girl in, he is fast asleep,' she cried.

The Princess was very down-hearted and walked slowly to his room. But when she opened the door, there he was sitting up in bed! She was so happy she ran and hugged him.

'The suffering is not yet over,' whispered the King. 'Tomorrow I shall be married to the Troll Hag and become a bear forever. The wedding procession will cross the drawbridge. If only we could cut the ropes of the drawbridge, we could be free from her and the spell would be broken.'

The Princess said, 'I think I have just the thing in my pocket.'

What did she have in her pocket? The claws, of course.

She set to work, sawing and scraping at the ropes with the sharp claws. When one claw was blunt she went on to the next, sawing and scraping all night long, until the ropes were as fine as four strands of hair.

The next morning the Troll Hag was dressed in her wedding gown, her head covered in a lacy veil. The trolls, dressed as bridesmaids and pageboys, scattered petals for the bride. Behind them lumbered the White Bear King. As the trolls crossed the drawbridge it began to shake. They tumbled off one by one. Then there was an almighty crack, and the whole bridge gave way beneath the Troll Hag. She plummeted down the mountain.

'AAAAAAAAHHHHHHHH!' she cried and broke into a thousand pieces!

There was only one troll left and that was the good servant. 'Somebody has to be King,' he said.

And a very good King he made, too.

Then the White Bear's skin fell away. He was wholly a man at last. He took the Princess by the hand and they found themselves at the bottom of the glass mountain.

On the way home they called in at the three cottages where the King introduced the Princess to her own three daughters.

'Now I understand,' said the Princess happily, 'why you were taken from me. So that you might help me find my own true love again.'

Then the King, and the Princess, and their three daughters had a real wedding which lasted nine days and nine nights, as true weddings do. Everybody was invited to it, including you. The cloth was spread, and you ate whatever you liked. The goblet was tipped, and you drank so much that you don't remember the party at all!

Pomme Clayton

Golden Star

There was once a king and queen who had twelve children, all boys. But one day, shortly before the queen was due to give birth to their thirteenth child, the king took her to a small room in the castle, unlocked the door and took her inside. In the room were twelve small coffins, each with a silk cushion in it.

'I have brought you here,' said the king, 'because I have decided that if our next child is a girl then I am going to kill all of our sons, so that she may inherit all of my wealth. These will be our sons' coffins.'

Now the queen was very upset when she heard this, but the king commanded her to say nothing of his plan to anyone and she didn't dare disobey him. They went out if the room, the king locked the door and he gave the key to the queen.

Now their youngest son was called Joseph and he spent most of his time with his mother. He noticed that she was very sad and asked her what the matter was.

'Don't ask,' she sighed. 'I can't tell you.'

But Joseph kept asking and asking, until at last the queen took him to the room, unlocked the door and showed him the coffins. She burst into tears and said, 'Your father has decided that if our next child is a girl, then you and your brothers are to be put to death and these will be your coffins.'

Now Joseph wasn't one to be upset by something like that.

'Don't worry,' he said. 'We'll go and hide in the forest until the baby is born. If it's a boy, raise a white flag on the castle and we'll know that it's safe to go home. But if it's a girl, raise a red flag and we'll go and live somewhere our father can't find us.'

So Joseph and his brothers went and hid in the forest and each day one of them would climb a tall tree and watch for a flag on the castle. On the twelfth day, it was Joseph's turn to be lookout. He climbed the tree and saw a red flag flying from the castle. Joseph scrambled back down the tree.

'Brothers, our mother has given birth to a girl,' he said, 'so we can never return home. We must go deep into the forest and live there.'

The brothers were all very angry that they could never return home. 'All our troubles have come to us because of a girl,' they said. 'Let us swear an oath to kill the first girl who crosses our path.'

They swore the oath and set off into the forest. When they had gone deep into the forest they found a house, set in a garden. The door was open and in they went. The house was clean and tidy but there was no sign of anyone living there. They moved into the house and there they lived very happily. Each day the eleven older brothers went out hunting, while Joseph stayed at home cooking and looking after the house.

Now, the daughter who had been born to the king and queen was a beautiful girl, with long blonde hair. On her forehead there was a golden star and so that's what they called her — Golden Star.

As Golden Star grew, it seemed that she became more beautiful every day. One day, when she was helping her mother and the other women with the washing, she noticed twelve small shirts.

'Whose are these?' she asked her mother. 'They're much too small to fit Father.'

The queen burst into tears and told her about her twelve brothers and how they had to flee when she was born. When she had heard the story, Golden Star said, 'All my brothers' troubles are on account of me. I'm going to search for them and I won't stop until I find them.'

And she left the castle straight away and began to search for her brothers. Eventually, after many adventures, she came to the house in the forest and knocked on the door. The eleven older brothers were out hunting and only Joseph was there, looking after the house. He opened the door and there stood Golden Star.

'Who are you?' he stammered in his amazement.

'My name is Golden Star,' she said, 'and I am looking for my twelve brothers who had to run away when I was born, and I won't stop searching until I find them.'

Joseph asked about her parents and when he was quite sure that she was indeed his sister he said, 'I'm Joseph, the youngest of your twelve brothers.'

They hugged each other and then sat talking of many things and delighting in each other's company. But then Joseph heard his brothers returning and he remembered the oath that they had sworn.

'Quick!' he said, opening the lid of a wooden trunk. 'Hide in here, for we have sworn to kill the first girl who crosses our path.'

Golden Star clambered quickly into the trunk and Joseph shut the lid, just as his brothers opened the door.

'And what have you found today?' Joseph asked his brothers.

'Well,' said his brothers, 'we've found these two hares and this pheasant.'

'Pah!' said Joseph. 'You have been out into the world and only found two hares and a pheasant, while I, by staying here, have found something much more valuable.'

'And what have you found?' asked the brothers.

'I'm not going to tell you,' said Joseph.

'Go on, tell us.'

'No.'

'Go on, go on.'

'No.'

'Go on, go on.'

And the more Joseph refused, the more curious the brothers became until, in the end, Joseph said, 'All right, I'll tell you, but only if you promise to do the first thing I ask you.'

'Yes, yes. We promise,' said the brothers, by this time beside themselves with curiosity.

'Very well,' said Joseph. 'Today our sister came to visit us and she's here now.'

'Where is she? Where is she?' screamed the brothers. 'We'll kill her.'

'Stop!' said Joseph. 'Remember your promise to me. And the first thing I ask you is to unswear the oath we swore to kill the first girl we met.'

The brothers had no choice but to do as he asked. Joseph opened the trunk and out stepped Golden Star. When the brothers saw her, they were delighted that Joseph had stopped them from killing her and they all lived happily together for some time, the older brothers going hunting while Golden Star and Joseph looked after the house.

One day, wishing to treat her brothers and give them a present, Golden Star went out into the garden and picked twelve lilies that were growing there, one for each of them. But, the moment she picked the flowers, her brothers all turned into ravens, the house and the garden disappeared, the ravens flew away and she found herself alone in the forest.

Then an old, old woman appeared and said, 'Tch, tch. That was a silly thing to do. You should never have picked those flowers. Now your brothers are ravens and nothing can save them.'

'Is there really nothing that can save them?' cried Golden Star.

'Well, there is one thing but it's much too hard for you. You'd never be able to do it, so there's no point in telling you.'

'Please, please tell me,' begged Golden Star. 'I'd do anything to save my brothers.'

'You'll never manage it. It's much too hard for the likes of you.'

'Please, please, please. I don't care how hard it is. I'll do it. I swear I will,' said Golden Star.

'Very well,' said the old woman. 'The only way to save your brothers is not to speak or smile or laugh for seven years. But I warn you, if it lacks just one minute of one hour of one day and you do speak or smile or laugh, then all your efforts will have been in vain and your brothers will be ravens forever. There, I told you it was too difficult for you to do!'

Golden Star said nothing and the old woman hobbled off into the forest, shaking her head. When she had gone, Golden Star climbed into a tree and there she sat. Now it happened that a young king was riding through the forest that day with his dogs, and the dogs ran up to the tree where Golden Star was sitting and started barking. The king looked up and saw Golden Star, fell in love with her and asked her to marry him. She said nothing, but merely nodded her head, climbed down the tree and together they rode back to his palace.

The king's mother, however, did not like this girl who never spoke nor smiled nor laughed, and tried everything she could think of to turn the king against her, but he wouldn't listen to her.

The years passed and the old queen kept whispering, whispering, whispering in the king's ear, 'I tell you that wife of yours is no good. She's a witch. Look at that golden star on her forehead, that's not normal is it? She never speaks or laughs, she never even smiles. Get rid of her. She's evil and means you no good.'

Year after year she whispered in the king's ear like that, and in the end he gave in and ordered Golden Star to be put to death. A great fire was built and she was tied to a stake in the middle of it. The king watched from a window as the fire was lit, tears streaming down his face, for he still loved her.

The flames licked higher and higher, closer and closer to Golden Star, but still she made no sound, spoke no word to defend herself. Just as the flames were about to touch her, twelve ravens flew out of the sun, landed by the fire and turned into the twelve brothers, for the seven years had now passed. The rushed into the fire and untied their sister.

Golden Star explained to the delighted king why she hadn't spoken, smiled or laughed in all those years. The old queen died of anger and Golden Star, her twelve brothers and the king lived happily ever after.

Tim Bowley

For dear life

The shells were flying over them, at them, in front of them, all day.

Edward had heard the voice calling his name from somewhere below where he was standing. He'd kept at his station, wincing at the sudden flashes that made brief, horrible days of the vile night. Through the insane noise, the insane light, he recalled sourly that it was his birthday.

The voice had come again. 'Edward. Oh my Edward.'

He ignored it. He'd noticed before that the hell they were living in could make things odd. Something would happen, like a shell exploding some way off, and you'd think of home, and church, and the vicar; or a day at school when you came second in the hundred yards. Or you'd remember, for no good reason that you could see, the blossom in your mother's garden.

This voice was like those things: sudden ordinary illusions it was best to ignore, or save for thinking about later, if there was going to be a later.

The shells were quieter, but still mad. How can we do this to each other? he wondered hopelessly for the hundredth time that month. We stand in filthy ditches and hurl fire at each other, and bits of metal fly about at a huge speed.

With each flash he glimpsed the trees ahead of him. They were skeletal and sad, still standing, but for no good reason. Sometimes he saw in the sudden light the path they had lain across the lake of water and mud. It looked like a rope of ammunition a giant might use, and was already broken in places. He stopped thinking about it, and remembered his home, where just now the forsythia would be opening in his mother's garden; where she would be shouting at the blackbirds that nibbled at the first crocuses.

The voice came again, urgently: 'Edward, oh Eddie....'

This time, he wasn't so sure about ignoring it. He stood still for a moment, shrugged – and turned and clambered down into the shelter where there was a roof propped up with rough pillars of wood. No-one was there. For a minute, he looked around. A rat scuttled across the floor. He was used to that, as he was to the vile smells of earth and decay, the smell of his own unwashed body.

There was a moment of great quiet, almost a silence.

From outside there came a crescendo of high-pitched scream, then a deafening bang, and a crash that died almost instantly away.

He trudged back to the trench. Where he had been standing had been wiped off the earth. Soil was scratched and thrown about for yards. If he'd still been there, he'd have been killed. He knelt to see what could be done for his friends.

Later, on leave, Edward told this story to his mother. They were sitting on deck chairs in the first warm days under the blossom Edward had waited for each spring ever since he could remember. Now some of it had settled on the arm of his uniform, like snow.

His mother listened, and then said: 'What day was this?'

Her eyes were staring at him in a trance.

He could remember the day because it had been his birthday. She interrupted him, 'It was about midday, and that's when you were born, and I couldn't take it any more, and I was so worried about you, and I just called your name several times and cried and cried and cried....'

More blossom dropped in the silent windless air. Edward looked at it, then at this mother. He got up, and hugged her for dear life, for dear life.

Fred Sedgwick

RIDDLES AND RUSES

The butterfly king

In a land both near and far from here, in a time before and after, there lived an old king. He wasn't a great king, nor was he a bad one. He just did his best and muddled along, much as the kings before him had done through countless generations.

The land he ruled was varied and bountiful, the people honest and hard-working. But all was not well with the kingdom. Far from it. For in the very centre of that land there lay a grim and terrible prison, patrolled day and night by a host of guards, for held within it was the Terror, the Unnamed One, put there so long ago that none could remember who or what or why it was.

Only the stories, handed down from generation to generation, gave a clue. The monster was held to be immortal, all-powerful, and should it ever break free, it was known that a terrible fate would fall on all the land.

A cold fear emanated from that prison, chilling the very air, and every so often a strange panic would grip the people and they would build up yet more defences to the prison. And so it had been, down through all the years of memory, until the time of our story.

Now the old king had a son, a lad of some sixteen summers. He was a merry and lively youth, strong in spirit but weak in body, for he had been born with a deformed leg, a misfortune put down to the curse of the monster, as all such things were. Many times the young prince dreamed that he was a great warrior, and would rid the land once and for all of the terror at its midst, but would awake each time to find his leg still bent and misshapen.

Now one day, the young prince was walking in the palace orchard, and as he walked he idly plucked and ate the ripe fruit from the trees. After a while, the sun being hot and his belly being full, he lay down in the shade of a great apple tree and closed his eyes and began to drift.

Then he became aware of a butterfly, flittering around him, though whether he saw it with his inner or his outer eye, he could not say. And as he watched, it seemed to him that the butterfly was speaking:

O Prince, become the Butterfly King,
Rise up and take the monster's sting,
In lands that are so far, so far,
You shall find just who you are,
Yes, you shall find just what you are,
Rise up and take the monster's sting,
O Prince, become the Butterfly King.

Awake now, the prince looked about him, but no sign of the butterfly could he see. Deeply troubled by this strange vision, the prince hobbled back to the palace and sought out his father.

The old king scratched his head and said, 'Well, I don't know what it means I'm sure, my boy. You'd better go and see Wise One.'

Wise One lived in a cave in the mountains, not far from the palace, but for the prince, with his crippled leg, it was a long and difficult journey.

Wise One watched the prince with piercing eyes, as he told his story. Could it be, could it really be, that here at last was the Butterfly King, prophesied of old?

When the prince had finished speaking, Wise One said nothing but sat a long time gazing into the fire. Suddenly, with frail old arms outstretched, Wise One gave a little cry, and in one hand there appeared a pearl, in the other a pouch with a butterfly design upon it.

Wise One put the pearl into the pouch and hung it around the prince's neck.

'You must leave the Kingdom at once,' said Wise One. 'Do not return to the palace nor take anything with you but this pearl I have given you. You will know how and when to use it. Go now, and let the wind blow you where it will.'

The prince left the cave of Wise One and went out on to the mountainside. A storm had broken there, and lightning flashed on the jagged peaks, while thunder rolled through the valleys and the rain poured down, driven by the howling. The prince looked longingly back at the warm cave, then taking a deep breath, he turned, and letting the wind blow on his back, he began his journey.

The Prince travelled on over land and sea, always following where the wild wind led him. North, south, east and west he went, and in all that time, he knew some moments of great joy, as when he glimpsed the sunlight on a distant waterfall, or heard the birds' early morning song, or sometimes, a wild animal would nuzzle up to him and briefly be his friend. But mainly it was hunger and thirst, heat and cold, and always the pain of his leg that were his travelling companions.

Now when four long and lonely years were passed, the prince found himself one day deep in a great forest, and as he walked beneath the huge beech trees, the wind that had blown on him unceasingly all those years, suddenly stopped.

Alert in every fibre of his being, the prince stopped too, and his ears, keen from all the perils of his journey, caught a tiny sound.

'Save me, O save me,' cried the voice.

Spinning around, the prince saw that it was a butterfly that called out, a butterfly caught in the web of a giant spider. The prince hurried towards it, but as he did so, the spider appeared. It was huge and ugly, and as it ran across its web it hissed:

The creature's mine, the creature's mine,
I'll eat your flesh, drink blood like wine.
Run for safety while you can
If you wish to stay a man.
Many hungry years long since
I ate another who was a prince.

Stooping to pick up a stick, his only weapon, the prince hobbled towards the spider and delivered a mighty blow, but it was the stick that broke and not the spider. Screaming its anger, the spider grew to ten times its already enormous size and rushed towards the prince. The prince backed away, searching desperately for some means of defence, but as he did so he stumbled, his leg gave way beneath him and he fell heavily to the ground. In a trice, the spider was on him, pinning him where he lay, its great mouth open, ready for the first poisonous bite.

'The pearl! The pearl!' called the butterfly.

The prince wrenched one arm free, put his hand into the pouch, pulled out the pearl and threw it into the spider's gaping mouth.

Immediately, the spider shrunk back to its original size and backed away, saying:

So be it,
The creature's yours.
The price is paid,
I fight no more.

Gingerly the prince got to his feet and, picking up a sharp stone, he very carefully cut the butterfly free from the web.

'Thank you, thank you,' said the butterfly, 'and now I shall repay you.'

And the butterfly began to beat her brightly coloured wings, and to sing a strange tune. Watching her, the prince began to feel drowsy, and lying down on the soft forest floor, he closed his eyes and let her song wash over him. He was dimly aware of something being wound around his tired body, but he had no power to resist, and soon he was fast asleep.

When he awoke, he felt renewed and refreshed, better than he had ever felt before. But then he realised that he was bound tightly about like a pea in a pod. He felt a moment of panic, but then, gathering his new found strength, he burst through the walls that bound him and emerged into the warm sunshine of morning.

The prince stretched and breathed deeply of the fresh forest air then, glancing down at his leg, he gasped! For he was indeed renewed and his leg, so long bent and misshapen, was now perfect and whole.

'Good morning, my prince,' said a gentle voice.

Turning around, the prince saw the most beautiful young woman he had ever seen.

I am the Princess of the Dell.
Now you have broken the spider's spell,
If you wish I'll be your bride,
And walk forever at your side.

Delighted, amazed, confused, the prince could only nod his head and hope never to wake from this wonderful dream. The princess took him by the hand and together they walked down the forest path. On and on they walked beneath the great green-leafed trees until they came at last to a lake, and at the edge of the lake there sat a frog.

Frog gazed at them with great black eyes and said:

O princess, I have a gift for you,
If you can but answer true.
Within these waters lies the prize,
Now show me that you are wise.

'What is harder than stone, yet softer than a summer's evening?' asked Frog.

'Truth,' replied the princess.

'And what may turn yet never moves?' asked Frog.

'The centre,' she said.

'And what may hurt, but can never, never harm?' croaked Frog.

'Love,' she smiled.

'Good, good, good,' said Frog. 'Now put your hand into the water and draw it out again.'

The princess put her hand into the lake, and as she took it out, all the water in her hand turned into a clear, clear crystal, a rainbow dancing on every face.

'Cover me up. Cover me up,' called the crystal. 'The time is not yet, the time is not yet.'

The princess took her silken scarf and, wrapping it around the crystal, placed it at her breast.

At that moment, in the prince's own land the old king died and, as he fell, the ground beneath the prison shook and trembled, and panic gripped the people.

'Aiyee! Aiyee! The monster escapes! The monster escapes! Build up the walls! Build up the walls or we shall die!'

Now that fear, that trembling of the earth, was felt by Frog so far away.

'The old king is dead. The monster stirs,' said Frog. 'With the princess and the crystal, you may yet save your land, but you must hurry. Go now. Go.'

The prince and the princess, with the crystal clasped to her breast, set out for their kingdom. For seven days and seven nights they ran without stopping. Like the wind they ran, across high and rugged mountains, through deep dark valleys; across hot and burning deserts and through thick and steaming swamps. On and on they ran until at last, they crossed the great river and came into their own land.

As they came into the kingdom, a piercing cold surrounded them, but the crystal would not let the cold enter into them. They crossed that land, now so deserted and desolate, and no living thing did they see, for all had fled before the icy terror.

On and on they went, until they came at last to the prison.

'Take me out! Take me out!' called the crystal. 'Now is the time. Now is the time.'

At once, the princess took the crystal, unwrapped it and held it high. Rainbows flashed from it, the ground beneath the prison shook and trembled, and all the outer walls of the prison fell to the ground.

'Again! Again!' called the crystal, and once more the princess held it high, and once more the rainbows flashed and the ground shook, and all the walls cracked and crumbled and fell as rubble on the ground.

Now all that remained was the very first prison. Squat and ugly it stood, built of massive unhewn rocks, the last defence between the world and the unknown terror within.

'Again! Again!' called the crystal, and without hesitation the Princess lifted it up as the rainbows flashed, and those mighty rocks burst asunder and fell as dust on the ground.

And there, there it lay, the Terror.

But it was not some huge-fanged, slimy monster that lay there, not some grim and gruesome demon, but a little, furry caterpillar.

'At last! At last!' sighed the caterpillar, and before their eyes it turned into a chrysalis, and from the chrysalis there emerged a beautiful butterfly with rainbow wings.

As the butterfly emerged, so a great warmth came from it and spread throughout the land, and in the twinkling of an eye, all the remains of the prison were turned into a summer garden, full of flowers and grasses, and birds and bees.

As it lay drying its wings in the warm sunshine, the butterfly spoke, 'You see, the very first king of this land placed me here. He had a fear of all things that crawled, I don't know why, and so without reason, he feared me. And not understanding what I would become, he placed me here. Since then, I have been the unknown terror at the heart of this land. Until now.'

So saying the butterfly spread its wonderful wings and flew away to feast on nectar.

The prince and princess became king and queen of that land, and long and wisely did they rule. They placed the crystal in the very centre of the land, where the prison had stood, and from it there bubbled forth a clear, clear stream of water, that runs to this very day.

Tim Bowley

Matiwara's name game

At the edge of the savannah there were lots of acacia trees. In the middle of the acacia trees, stood a small house with a thorny fence. A mysterious Old Woman lived in the house. Nobody knew anything about her. Nobody visited her but there were lots of stories about her in all the nearby villages. There was a little girl called Matiwara living with the Old Woman. Where did she come from? Who was she? Nobody knew anything about her. One of the stories talked about a spell cast on Matiwara by the Old Woman so that Matiwara could never leave her.

Matiwara did all the housework for the Old Woman. She cleaned the house, dusted the house, gathered firewood and cooked for the Old Woman.

The Old Woman was always angry and never happy with Matiwara. This made Matiwara very miserable.

'Please tell me how I can set myself free and live in a village like all the other people,' Matiwara asked the Old Woman.

Haa Haa Haa, Hee Hee Hee,
You can never set yourself free.

Sang the Old Woman and curled up by the fire to go to sleep.

This went on for a few days and a few nights.

One night Matiwara cooked the Old Woman's favourite dinner which was fried corn with grated coconut, yellow guavas and ripe mangoes. It was delicious and the Old Woman was really very happy after eating it. Matiwara took this opportunity to ask her again.

'Please, dear lady, tell me the secret to set myself free.'

Haa Haa Haa, Hee Hee Hee,
You'll never guess that to be free
You must find the name given to me.

Sang the old lady.

Matiwara jumped for joy. She set to work, guessing and collecting names from that very evening. Every day Matiwara sat by the fire after a long day's hard work and tried to guess the Old Woman's name.

'Is your name Rampala, Jumbona, Sabina, Deggee, Mambo or Sabulana?' asked Matiwara.

'No, no, no,' replied the Old Woman.

'Is your name…?' *(At this point the audience takes part in providing names for the Old Woman. Some names can be made up by children and adults, and some can be names from different cultures. The idea is to try out as many different, interesting and exciting names as possible.)*

'You can try, try, try, but you cannot find my name. It is a big secret. Only I know my name and I'll never tell it to anyone ever, ever in my life.'

Matiwara was very disappointed. She could not eat or sleep. She could not finish her day's work. The Old Woman was always angry with her.

One day Matiwara forgot to collect the firewood so she had to rush into the woods to collect it before dark. She soon lost her way and went deeper and deeper into the woods. It was beginning to get dark. Matiwara had to hurry up and find her way back when she suddenly came across a clearing in the woods. She hid behind an acacia tree. She could see a fire burning in the middle of the clearing. There was nobody about.

She stood very still and listened.

She could hear the night calls of the animals.

Suddenly... a loud cackle shook the silence.

The Old Woman appeared from behind the trees carrying some acacia thorns. She threw them on the fire and the flames leapt up high.

The Old Woman then began to dance round the fire singing.

Haa Haa Haa, Hee Hee Hee
She'll never guess it,
She'll never be free.
She must find the name given to me.
Haa Haa Haa, Hee Hee Hee,
It's Shokolokobangoshey. It's
Shokolokobangoshey.

Matiwara heard the name clearly. She almost shouted out for joy but she slowly crept away and made her way back to the house.

The Old Woman arrived, looking very tired and asked Matiwara, 'Have you got my soup ready?'

'No, I have been busy finding new names for you today,' replied Matiwara.

'Oh. Oh. You have been naughty. I am going to punish you. Where is my stick?' and the old lady started to look for her stick.

'Is your name Aaa Zoom Big a Zum?' asked Matiwara.

'No, no,' replied the Old Woman. 'And I am tired and hungry. Give me my dinner quickly.'

'Just one more then,' pleaded Matiwara. 'Is your name – eh – Shoko, Shokoloko – Shokolokobangoshey?'

Lightning flashed across the sky and lit up the acacia trees....

'No, no, yes,' said the Old Woman as she stood still. 'I am Shokolokobangoshey.'

Lightning flashed again. Matiwara closed her eyes and found herself in her own village with her own family. She had forgotten everything about the Old Woman.

A strong wind blew and the Old Woman disappeared in the tall sandy grass of the savannah.

Nobody has ever seen her again. But the villagers say that if you stand on the edge of the savannah, you can hear 'Shokolokobangoshey, Shokolokobangoshey' as the wind blows through the tall sandy savannah grass.

Usha Bahl

The story with no ending

Once long, long ago in a distant land, there was a king who loved stories. He loved hearing them all day long, so much so that whenever his treasurer asked him about how he should raise money through taxes, he didn't reply – he found such things so boring. When people came to him for a judgement on a dispute over who was the rightful owner of a piece of land, the King wasn't interested. All he wanted to hear about was stories, especially ones he had never heard before.

Naturally, his storytellers had to work hard, so hard in fact that they used up all the stories they knew. The King was desperate for new stories. When his merchants sailed their ships to trade in distant lands, he wasn't bothered about what goods they brought back. 'Bring me back some new stories,' he told them. He gave the same command to his soldiers if they had to go to war.

But slowly the stories dried up, and the King began to despair, until one day he had what he thought was a brilliant idea. If someone could tell him a story that never ended, he need never worry again about not having new stories. At once, he had posted throughout the kingdom notices which said:

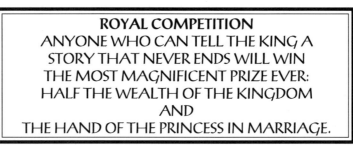

> **ROYAL COMPETITION**
> ANYONE WHO CAN TELL THE KING A
> STORY THAT NEVER ENDS WILL WIN
> THE MOST MAGNIFICENT PRIZE EVER:
> HALF THE WEALTH OF THE KINGDOM
> AND
> THE HAND OF THE PRINCESS IN MARRIAGE.

People were naturally very interested when they read this, but when their eyes reached the small print at the bottom of the notice, they read: Anyone who tells a story that has an ending will have his head cut off.

So no-one entered the competition, and as the weeks passed, the King felt worse than ever.

But one day a stranger came to the palace gates and announced that he had a story that had no ending. He was immediately taken to the King who eagerly said, 'Right, my man, don't delay. Let's hear it straight away.'

'Excuse me, your Majesty,' said the stranger holding up one hand. 'Before I begin the story, I must insist on you agreeing to two conditions.'

'Well, state your conditions and we shall see,' said the King impatiently.

'My first condition is that there will be no interruptions,' said the stranger.

'But I love listening to stories. I never interrupt them,' insisted the King. 'I agree to that condition. What is your other condition?'

'My second condition, your Majesty, is that I shall be allowed to tell the story in my own way.'

'Of course,' said the King. 'All storytellers tell stories in their own way. I agree to that. Now can we begin?'

So everyone settled down, and the storyteller began.

'Once upon a time, there was a wise and wealthy king, much like yourself, your Majesty,' (The King liked the sound of this story and he began to relax.) 'who ruled his country well. However, there was a great problem in that land, for every so often the rains of spring and summer failed to come, so there would be a drought. No crops would grow and there would be a famine from which many died. The King thought hard about this and decided that if a giant granary was built to store the grains of corn after a good harvest, then his country would have food in reserve if the following summer brought another drought.

'So that year the builders built an enormous granary on the outskirts of the town, and when it was built they waited to see if the harvest was good. It turned out to be a bumper harvest, the best for years, and so the granary was filled up completely with grains of corn.

'When it was full, they sealed up the windows and sealed up the doors until not a single crack was showing. Well, there was in fact one crack where a piece of masonry around a window had come loose, but that crack was so small that only an ant could have got through it.

'I don't know if you have seen ants at work, how they team up and carry quite large objects – well, there were lots of ants in this land and one of them went through the crack, took a grain of corn and then came out. Then another ant went through the crack, took a grain of corn and then came out. And then another ant went through the crack, took a grain of corn and then came out....'

Suddenly the King exploded with impatience. 'Look, forget about the ants and the grains of corn and get on with the story!'

'Your Majesty!' The storyteller looked shocked. 'You did agree that there were to be no interruptions.'

The King was embarrassed. He had broken his royal word. 'I beg your pardon – I won't interrupt again.'

'And you also agreed, your Majesty, that I should be allowed to tell the story in my own way.'

'Yes, yes, of course,' said the King. 'You must go on in your own way – but before you do, could you tell me if there are many more grains of corn in the granary?'

'Millions, your Majesty.'

'And lots of ants to come, I suppose,' said the King sadly.

'Billions, your Majesty.'

'Oh dear,' said the King. 'Carry on with the story.'

So the storyteller continued.

'And another ant went through the crack, took a grain of corn and then came out....'

The ants went on taking the grains of corn all that day, so that when it was time for supper and bed, the King was really relieved.

The next morning they gathered together in the same place.

The King raised his hand and said, 'Before you start, are there still many more grains of corn left?'

'Millions, your Majesty.'

'And ants?'

'Trillions, your Majesty.' (They must have been arriving all night.)

'Oh dear,' said the King. 'Carry on with the story.'

And the storyteller continued.

'And another ant went through the crack, took a grain of corn and then came out....'

He went on all that day, and the next. He went on all week, and all through the next week ant after ant went through the crack and took the corn.

Meanwhile the King found that he was able to follow the story without really listening – his eyes just glazed over. And when his treasurer crept up beside him and whispered about a problem he had with raising taxes, the King listened and whispered back his decision. Then when other people came and whispered about their disputes over land ownership, the King found that really interesting and he whispered back his judgement. In fact, as the weeks went by, the King began to rule the country much better than he had ever done before.

One day, just as the storyteller was saying, 'And another ant...,' the King jumped up and cried, 'Stop!'

'But, your majesty, you promised...,' began the storyteller.

'No, no,' said the King, 'I am not interrupting. I am stopping the story. You have indeed told a story that never ends, but please, please, don't tell it any more. You have won the competition.'

And so that's how the storyteller won half the kingdom and married the princess.

After that the King became a much better king, and when he died, his daughter and the storyteller became Queen and King in his place, and they say that they were the wisest rulers ever. And they also say that when anyone tells this story, as I have told it to you, that just shows that the story still hasn't ended after all these years.

So the story really is the story that never ends, and if you go away and tell it to someone else, then it still won't have ended.

THE END (Well, not really.)

Tony Aylwin

Penteclemas and the Pea

There was a man called Penteclemas and he was walking along the road, going nowhere in particular. He walked along and he walked along; and the sun shone and the birds sang. But Penteclemas wasn't really listening to them because he was thinking about food. He was a poor man and he'd had nothing for his breakfast but an apple taken from a wayside tree. And because he had no shoes he was thinking about his feet, which he'd wrapped in pieces of old sacking.

But he walked along and he walked along, whistling as he went. He was a happy sort of a fellow, in spite of everything.

And he walked along and he walked along, and there, in the middle of the path, he saw a pea! He picked it up and put it in his pocket. There was plenty of room because there was nothing else in there.

He thought to himself, 'I'll plant this pea, and when it's grown there will be lots of pea-pods, each one with five or six peas, or even more. And I'll plant all those. And when they're grown there will be thousands of peas. And I'll plant all *those* and when *they've* grown there'll be millions of peas. And then I'll sell them in all the cities, and I'll become rich.'

And on he walked, whistling away as tuneful as any bird, imagining to himself all the things he'd do when he was rich. Suddenly a thought hit him: 'How will I be able to transport all the peas? I'll need a fleet of lorries and a couple of ships. But where will a man like me get all that? Oh, I know. I'll ask the king.'

So on he walked. And at the next corner he turned left, taking the path that led to the highway that led to the royal palace.

He hadn't walked more than a mile or so, when he heard a great roaring up ahead. And there, looking amazing against the blue sky, was a green and red dragon, flying straight towards him. Well, it was the most fearsomest dragon you ever saw. It measured (head to tail) from where I'm sitting right out of the door and most of the way down the path. It had two huge wings and a long pointiferous tail, and several rows of sharp ugly teeth. Its eyes were like two fog-lights, and as it sailed along it breathed out great licks of fire; and it polluted all the blue with black, horrible smoke.

It flew right up to him, landed in the field beside him and spoke to him over the hedge.

'Hallo,' it said.

'Hallo,' said Penteclemas.

'What's your name?' it said.

'Penteclemas,' said Penteclemas.

'How do you spell that?' said the dragon.

'I don't know,' said Penteclemas. 'I ain't no scholar.'

'Where are you going?' said the dragon.

'To the king's palace,' said Penteclemas.

'What for?' said the dragon.

'To ask for the loan of a fleet of lorries and a couple of ships.'

'Oh,' said the dragon.

'Ah,' said Penteclemas.

'You see that castle?' said the dragon.

Penteclemas looked up to the hill-top. It was crowned with a fantastic castle, all turrets and battlements and slit windows and portcullises.

'Yes, I see it,' said Penteclemas

'Well, that castle belongs to me, at present,' said the dragon. 'But if you can guess three riddles that I shall ask you in three days time, it'll become yours, because I shall have to burst.'

'That's nice,' said Penteclemas.

'But if you can't guess the riddles,' said the dragon, 'I shall eat you.'

'All right,' said Penteclemas. Well, what else could he say?

'All *right*!' said the dragon, and it clapped its wings and away it flew.

'Well,' thought Penteclemas, 'What an exciting morning!'

And he walked on and he walked on. It doesn't take long to tell, but it was a good while before he reached the king's palace. He rang the bell on the gate and was taken in to see the king.

'What can I do for you?' says the king.

'I want the loan of a fleet of lorries and a couple of ships,' says Penteclemas.

'What for?' says the king, looking at the shabby way Penteclemas was dressed, and wondering to himself.

'That's a confidential secret,' says Penteclemas. 'But if I do not appear rich now,' he added, winking heavily at the king, 'I shall appear rich soon.' He was thinking of the pea, you see.

But the king was puzzled by this answer. 'Perhaps this is a rich man in disguise as a poor man, and if so, perhaps he's the fellow to marry my daughter,' he thought to himself. 'He certainly doesn't look like the others.'

Now the king's daughter was rather a bother to him. She was clever and helpful and kind and pretty. But she had a mind of her own. When various of the local princes had proposed marriage to her she had just laughed and said no.

'If you're a rich man in disguise as a poor man,' said the king, 'I have a daughter who might suit you.'

Well, this came as a bit of a surprise to Penteclemas and for a moment he didn't know what to say. 'Well, what's she like?' he said at last.

'She's all right,' said the king. 'Oh look, here she comes now.' And in came the princess.

As a matter of fact she'd been listening outside the door and she'd rather liked the sound of Penteclemas. When she came in and saw the ragged sunburnt man, she gave him a big smile. He smiled back.

'What do you think?' said the king.

'All right,' said Penteclemas.

Well, what else could be say?

Later on, the king gave Penteclemas a big supper, and that was all right with him, too. He'd had nothing since the apple. Then the king sent Penteclemas and the princess into the other room to talk to each other. And they got on like a house on fire. She'd never met anybody at all like him; and he'd only heard about princesses in stories. But that didn't bother them. They talked of this and they talked of that, and the time flew by like anything. But Penteclemas never mentioned the pea and the dragon. Well, why should he?

Meanwhile the king was talking to the chief servant. 'I want you to make up a bed for this stranger. Give him a lumpy mattress and a straw pillow and torn blankets. And I want you to watch while he sleeps. If he can sleep on that, he is obviously used to that kind of a bed. So he's a poor man and he can't marry the princess.'

The chief servant made up the bed as he had been told. Then he hid in the bedroom cupboard.

'Time for bed now,' said the king to Penteclemas, and off they all went upstairs.

Well, the next morning the servant went and told the king, 'That Penteclemas, he never slept a wink all night. Tossing and turning he was, this way and that from bed time to cock crow.'

'Good,' said the king. 'Now you get some rest yourself and tonight I want you to make up a bed with a down mattress, a soft, soft pillow, cosy blankets and a silk coverlet; and watch again. And we'll see how he sleeps on that.'

So the servant did as he was told. The next day he reported to the king, 'That Penteclemas, he slept all night as soundly as a day-old child.'

'Good,' said the king. 'That proves he's used to that kind of a bed and he's a rich man. So he can marry my daughter.'

That was the way the king thought.

But the reason Penteclemas had not slept the first night was that he kept trying to hide the pea in the raggy blankets. He kept losing it, then looking for it, then hiding it again. So that he never got a moment's sleep. And the reason he slept so well the next night was that he was so tired, not having slept the night before, that he couldn't keep awake, pea or no pea. But the king wasn't to know that.

So Penteclemas and the king's daughter were married.

Then Penteclemas thought to himself, 'Well here I am, married to a princess. How am I going to look after her? Oh yes, of course. There's the fortune I'm going to make from my pea.'

After a while he began to think about that dragon. 'How am I going to guess the riddles? I've never guessed a riddle right in all my life.'

He became sad and thoughtful. The princess asked her husband what was the matter.

'Nothing,' he replied, sighing and staring at the floor.

So she became sad and thoughtful, too. Then Eleanor, the princess's old nurse, who had looked after her since she was a baby, saw that the princess was unhappy, on the one day of her life when she ought to be happiest of all.

'What's the matter, my little cherry tree?' Eleanor asked her. 'Why are you so sad and thoughtful?'

'My husband is sad, so I am sad, too,' said the princess.

So Eleanor went to Penteclemas and asked him, 'Why are you sad?'

'Oh. No reason,' said he.

But she kept on at him and kept on at him and bothered him and pestered him and at last he told her everything; all about the dragon and the riddles.

'Is that all?' said Eleanor, laughing. 'We'll soon see about that dragon. Riddles indeed! Fiddle-de-dee!'

So Penteclemas cheered up.

Well, it wasn't that much later that there was a great roaring commotion in the sky and the dragon flew along and landed in the palace gardens, singeing the lawn something terrible as he did so.

He walked up to the double doors and was shown into a hall. There was nothing in it but a big oak cupboard. The dragon glared about him, then said in a terrible voice, 'Where are you, Penteclemas?'

Now Penteclemas and the nurse, Eleanor, were hiding together inside the cupboard. Penteclemas answered in a quaking voice, 'I'm here in this cupboard, and I'm not coming out. You'll easily enough be able to break down the doors if I can't guess your riddles.'

'Well,' thinks the dragon, 'that's true enough.' Then he says aloud, 'Are you ready for the first riddle?'

'I'm ready,' says Penteclemas.

So the dragon puffs out a little smoke and asks the first riddle. And this was it:

Little thin Bess
In a white dress
And a red nose.
The longers she stands
The shorter she grows.

'That's easy,' whispered Eleanor. 'It's a candle.'

'That's easy!' shouted Penteclemas. 'It's a candle!'

'All right,' said the dragon. 'You needn't shout. I'm not deaf. I bet you can't guess this one.'

And he shouts out, but not quite so loudly:

Though not an ox I have horns;
Though not an ass I carry a pack-saddle;
And wherever I go I leave silver behind me.

'I'm not an ass, either,' whispered Eleanor. 'It's a snail.'

'I'm no ass, either,' shouted Penteclemas. 'It's a nail.'

'A *snail*,' whispered Eleanor.

'I mean a *snail*!' shouted Penteclemas.

'That's funny,' thought the dragon to himself. 'He didn't look that clever when he was walking along the road. I wish I'd chosen someone else, now.'

It never struck him, you see, that there was someone else in the cupboard *with* Penteclemas. Then the dragon spat out a lick of fire to keep his voice from trembling, because he knew that if Penteclemas guessed the next riddle he would have to burst. Then with a horrible snarl he said: 'I *dare* you to guess this one:

I have no tongue
Yet I answer faithfully;

None has ever seen me
Yet everyone hears me.

'It's an echo,' whispered the nurse.

Penteclemas repeated in a loud firm voice: 'It's an echo!'

So then the dragon had to burst. He did it with such a BANG! that the door of the cupboard flew open and Penteclemas and Eleanor came dancing out. But the dragon didn't see that, because he was dead.

After that Penteclemas got the dragon's castle and all the treasure that was in it, which was a great lot. He and the princess gave Eleanor the nurse a chest full of diamonds, sapphires, emeralds and gold pieces. So she was all right.

Then the two of them settled down to live their lives.

And a happy life they lived together.

All because of a pea!

As for the pea, on the very next day Penteclemas went into the garden and planted it. But a mouse came and ate it up.

So that was the end of that.

Gerard Benson

Two boys eating nuts

Once upon a time there lived two boys. One was called Pirichan[1] Pich, the other was called Pirichan Mor.

One day they went gathering walnuts from a walnut tree. Pirichan Mor climbed up among the branches of the tree, picked the nuts and threw them down to Pirichan Pich. Pirichan Pich sat on the ground beneath the branches of the tree and caught the nuts as they came down, and cracked them with his little hammer.

But all the nuts that Pirichan Pich cracked, he ate, so that when Pirichan Mor climbed down from the tree there were no nuts left for him at all.

'Half those nuts were mine,' he said. 'I'm going to find a stick and I'm going to whack and thwack you for that.'

So off went Pirichan Mor in search of a stick.

Soon he found one, growing from the branch of a tree, so he said to the tree:

I need a stick both hard and straight
To whack and thwack poor Pirichan Pich
Who ATE MY NUTS!

'Well, certainly and of course,' said the tree, but first you must find an axe with which to cut me.'

So off went Pirichan Mor in search of an axe.

Soon he found one, lying beside a pile of wood chippings on the floor of the forest, and so he said to the axe:

I need an axe of heavy weight,
To cut the stick both hard and straight,
To whack and thwack poor Pirichan Pich
Who ATE MY NUTS!

1. The 'ch' in Pirichan is pronounced as in 'loch'

'By all means,' said the axe, 'but can't you see I'm blunt? First you must find a sharpening stone with which to grind me.'

So off went Pirichan Mor in search of a sharpening stone.

Soon he found one, lying among the pebbles beside the lake, and so he said to the stone:

I need a rough-edged sharpening stone
To grind the axe of heavy weight,
To cut the stick both hard and straight,
To whack and thwack poor Pirichan Pich
Who ATE MY NUTS!

'I'm yours for the using,' said the sharpening stone, 'but first you must find some water with which to wet me.'

So Pirichan Mor knelt down by the wide blue water of the lake and called out to it:

I need some water from the lake
To wet the rough-edged sharpening stone,
To grind the axe of heavy weight,
To cut the stick both hard and straight,
To whack and thwack poor Pirichan Pich
Who ATE MY NUTS!

'Well and good,' said the lake, 'and you can have as much of my water as you like, but first you must find a great-antlered stag to swim across me.'

So off went Pirichan Mor in search of a stag.

Soon he found one, deep in a green thicket of the forest, and so he said to the stag:

I need a stag with antlers great
To swim across the lapping lake,
To wet the rough-edged sharpening stone,
To grind the axe of heavy weight,
To cut the stick both hard and straight,
To whack and thwack poor Pirichan Pich
Who ATE MY NUTS!

'I will never swim the lake,' said the stag, 'unless you find a fast-footed hunting dog to chase me to it.'

So off went Pirichan Mor in search of a dog.

Soon he found one, curled up in a kennel, with ears pricked and one eye open, and so he said to the dog:

I need a dog both fast and fleet
To chase the stag with antlers great,
To swim across the lapping lake,
To wet the rough-edged sharpening stone,
To grind the axe of heavy weight,
To cut the stick both hard and straight,
To whack and thwack poor Pirichan Pich
Who ATE MY NUTS!

'Gladly will I chase the stag,' said the dog, 'but first you must rub soft, yellow butter into my four feet.'

So off went Pirichan Mor in search of the butter.

Soon he found some, in a china dish on the farmhouse kitchen table, and so he said to the butter:

I need some butter soft and sweet
To rub into the fast dog's feet,
To chase the stag with antlers great,
To swim across the lapping lake,
To wet the rough-edged sharpening stone,
To grind the axe of heavy weight,
To cut the stick both hard and straight,
To whack and thwack poor Pirichan Pich
Who ATE MY NUTS!

'I'm yours for the taking,' said the butter, 'but first you must find a mouse to scrape me.'

So off went Pirichan Mor in search of a mouse.

Soon he found one, nibbling at the crumbs on the farmhouse pantry floor, and so he said to the mouse:

I need a mouse with nibbling teeth
To scrape the butter soft and sweet,
To rub into the fast dog's feet,
To chase the stag with antlers great,
To swim across the lapping lake,
To wet the rough-edged sharpening stone,
To grind the axe of heavy weight,
To cut the stick both hard and straight,
To whack and thwack poor Pirichan Pich
Who ATE MY NUTS.

'I will only scrape the butter,' said the mouse, 'if you can find a fat, black cat, to chase me to it.'

So off went Pirichan Mor in search of a cat.

Soon he found one, curled up and purring on the warm tiles of the barn roof, and so he said:

I need a cat as black as night
To chase the mouse with nibbling teeth,
To scrape the butter soft and sweet,
To rub into the fast dog's feet,
To chase the stag with antlers great,
To swim across the lapping lake,
To wet the rough-edged sharpening stone,
To grind the axe of heavy weight,
To cut the stick both hard and straight,
To whack and thwack poor Pirichan Pich
Who ATE MY NUTS!

'Chasing mice is my delight,' said the cat, 'but first, bring me a saucerful of milk for I am thirsty.'

So off went Pirichan Mor in search of a cow.

Soon he found one, chewing slowly in the green meadow, and so he said:

I need your creamy milk so white
To give to the cat as black as night,
To chase the mouse with nibbling teeth,
To scrape the butter soft and sweet,
To rub into the fast dog's feet,
To chase the stag with antlers great,

To swim across the lapping lake,
To wet the rough-edged sharpening stone,
To grind the axe of heavy weight,
To cut the stick both hard and straight,
To whack and thwack poor Pirichan Pich
Who ATE MY NUTS!

'There's plenty of milk and more,' said the cow, 'and you can have as much as you like, but first bring me some corn from the barn.'

So off went Pirichan Mor in search of some corn.

Soon he found the stable boy, sweeping the chaff from the floor of the barn, and so he said:

I need some corn for the cow to eat
To get the creamy milk so white,
To give to the cat as black as night,
To chase the mouse with nibbling teeth,
To scrape the butter soft and sweet,
To rub into the fast dog's feet,
To chase the stag with antlers great,
To swim across the lapping lake,
To wet the rough-edged sharpening stone,
To grind the axe of heavy weight,
To cut the stick both hard and straight,
To whack and thwack poor Pirichan Pich
Who ATE MY NUTS!

'There's stooks and stacks and sacks of corn to spare,' said the stable boy, 'but first you must run to the baker's shop and bring me a bun, warm from the oven.'

So off went Pirichan Mor to the baker's shop.

And there was the baker, weighing flour into a great mixing bowl, and so he said:

I need a bun for the boy to bite
To get the corn for the cow to eat,
To get the creamy milk so white,
To give to the cat as black as night,
To chase the mouse with nibbling teeth,
To scrape the butter soft and sweet,
To rub into the fast dog's feet,
To chase the stag with antlers great,
To swim across the lapping lake,
To wet the rough-edged sharpening stone,
To grind the axe of heavy weight,
To cut the stick both hard and straight,
To whack and thwack poor Pirichan Pich
Who ATE MY NUTS!

'Cherry buns and currant buns and buns of every kind,' said the baker, 'but first I need some water to wet the flour to make the dough for the buns.'

And the baker gave Pirichan Mor a sieve and told him to go to the well and fetch him some water.

So off went Pirichan Mor to the well, and he dipped the sieve into the water. But when he lifted the sieve, the water ran straight through the holes of it and back into the well. He tried again and the same thing happened.

Poor Pirichan Mor!

He threw the sieve on to the ground, put his hands over his face and the hot tears came trickling down between his fingers. Just then, high overhead, a great white seagull came flying.

'Rub soft black mud to it,' the seagull cried. 'Rub soft black mud to it.'

So Pirichan Mor found some soft black mud, and he rubbed the mud into the sieve until all the holes were filled, and then he left the sieve in the sunshine, and when the mud was dry and hard he dipped the sieve into the well again. But the water washed the mud from the holes of the sieve, and it ran straight through and back into the well, just as it had before.

Poor Pirichan Mor!

He threw the sieve on to the ground, put his hands over his face and the hot tears came trickling down between his fingers. Just then, high overhead, a raggedy black crow came flying.

'Rub sticky brown clay to it,' the black crow cried. 'Rub sticky brown clay to it.'

So Pirichan Mor found some sticky brown clay, and he rubbed the clay into the holes of the sieve until all of them were filled, and he left the sieve in the sunshine.

And when the clay was dry and hard he dipped the sieve into the well again, and this time the clay stayed firm. And when Pirichan Mor lifted the sieve from the well, there was not a trickle of water from it.

Carefully, without spilling a drop, Pirichan Mor carried the water to the baker's shop. And the baker used the water to make the dough to bake the buns. And he gave Pirichan Mor two of them, warm from the oven. Well, Pirichan Mor ate one of those buns, but he gave the other to the stable boy,

Who gave him the corn for the cow to eat,
Who gave him the creamy milk so white,
Which he gave to the cat as black as night,
Who chased the mouse with nibbling teeth,
Who scraped the butter soft and sweet,
Which he rubbed into the fast dog's feet,
Who chased the stag with antlers great,
Who swam across the lapping lake,
Which wetted the rough-edged sharpening stone,
Which ground the axe of heavy weight,
Which cut the stick both hard and straight,
Which whacked and thwacked poor Pirichan Pich
Who ATE HIS NUTS!

Hugh Lupton

Sir Gawain and the loathly lady

King Arthur had been defeated in single combat by a supernatural knight. This knight had agreed to spare the king's life on condition that he promised to return in a year and a day with the answer to the question 'What is it that women desire most of all?' And if he should fail to find the right answer, then the knight would cut off the king's head.

So Arthur set off straight away with his nephew Gawain, on a quest to save the king's life. For a year they travelled the length and breadth of the kingdom and everywhere they went they asked if anyone knew the answer to the riddle.

Well, some said this and some said that and some said something else. In fact, everyone they spoke to said something different. They collected a great list of answers but, deep inside, they knew that none of them was the right one. The year was over, the quest had failed, and with heavy hearts they set off for the place where Arthur was to meet the knight and lose his head.

As they were riding through the forest, they saw lights, dancing on the ground ahead of them, at a crossroads. As they got nearer, the lights disappeared and when they got to the crossroads, all that they found there was an old, old woman, a crone, dressed all in black, with a black hood over her head. As they passed, the crone threw back her hood and greeted them.

Now this old crone was UGLY! Not just ordinary, everyday ugly, but ugly in a way that turns the stomach and makes for nightmares. Her face was like a skull and the putrid flesh that hung from it was sickly yellow and scaly like a fish; from her slit of a mouth protruded teeth like tusks, black and rotting; her sunken eyes glowed red like burning coals; her filthy hair hung like snakes, crawling with lice; her twisted body was barely recognisable as human and she smelt so bad that the horses shied away.

'And where are you off to, my fine young sirs?' lisped the crone, in a voice like fingernails on a blackboard.

'We are on a quest,' said Arthur, fighting for breath in the rancid air.

'Quest indeed!' cackled the crone. 'From what I hear, you've failed to find

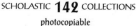

the answer to the riddle and will lose your pretty head.'

'We have a long list of answers,' answered Arthur, with a confidence he did not feel.

'What good is that,' screeched the crone, 'when none of them is the right one?'

'If you know that much, do you also know the right answer?' asked Arthur, hope rising.

'Indeed I do! Nothing simpler!' grated the crone, 'but I won't tell you what it is unless one of your knights promises to marry me.'

'What!, gasped Arthur. 'I don't wish to be rude, but I couldn't possibly ask one of my knights to marry you.'

'Suit yourself!' she snapped, pulling the hood back over her head.

'If you give us the true answer, then I will marry you,' said Gawain, spurring his horse forward.

The crone looked up, fixing Gawain with blazing eyes, and out of her twisted mouth asked, 'Sure?'

'I swear it,' answered Gawain.

'Very well then. The answer you seek is this: What women desire most of all is power over their own lives.'

Arthur wrote this down at the end of the list, hoping that his enemy would find another answer that satisfied him before he came to this one, thus sparing Gawain from his terrible fate.

They rode on to the meeting place, and waiting for them was the supernatural knight. They gave him the list of answers they had collected and as he sat there reading through it, he chuckled to himself. 'No, not that one... not that one... nor that....' The nearer he got to the end, the louder he laughed, until he came to the last answer on the list and his face fell.

'Yes, that's it. The last one,' he stormed, throwing the paper down.

'Told you!' cackled the crone. 'And now, Gawain, let's get married straight away.'

The three of them returned to the palace, where the wedding was held and a dismal affair it was, for all grieved for the fate of Gawain. When it was over, Gawain and his bride went to their room and the crone got into bed.

'Gawain,' she wheezed, 'This must be a true marriage. Kiss me.'

Gawain held his breath and went over to the bed. He closed his eyes, bent down and kissed her.

'There, that wasn't so bad was it?' said a gentle voice. 'Open your eyes and look at me.'

And when Gawain looked, lying there was the most beautiful woman he had ever seen.

'I can only keep this form for half of every day,' she said. 'Now you must choose. Do you want me to be like this during the day and do you honour in the court, or ugly during the day and beautiful at night when we are alone together?'

'Lady,' said Gawain, 'that choice I leave to you.'

At that she hugged him and said, 'That is the right answer. Now I shall be my beautiful self all of the time.'

Tim Bowley

A-riddle-a-ring-a-roses

There was, there was not.
Not here, not there.
Where then? Wait, and you'll hear.

There was a woman and a man, a husband and wife. They lived, laughed, talked, worked, did everything together. They were very much in love.

Do you know what they did for work? They were gardeners. Do you know what they grew? Roses, of course. And what colour roses? Only red ones, beautiful, bright blood-red roses.

Every evening they would stand together at the door of their house, and look out over their garden, enjoying the sweet scent of rose, enjoying the sweet sight of red sweeping as far as the eye could see. Truly life was rosy.

Till one day, without warning, without reason, without any clues as to why or how, the woman disappeared. The man searched the house from top to bottom, he searched the garden from front to back, he searched through his mind, turned it inside out. Nothing. Not a trace.

So, as he had nothing to go on, there was nothing he could do. Except wait. And hope. And work, to take his mind off waiting and hoping. The days dragged by into weeks. The weeks crawled into months. The months stumbled on towards a year.

Then one night, very late, he was sitting downstairs, head in his hands. Scratch, scratch, scratch, he heard something at the window. He looked out and what did he see? There was his wife, very pale, very thin, but alive.

He brought her in, he sat her by the fire, he held her in his arms. 'Where have you been? I couldn't eat, I couldn't sleep.'

'No more could I,' she said. 'I didn't want to leave you; I couldn't bear to lose you. But THEY were jealous of our happiness. The hidden folk, the hidden forces, call them what you will, took me away and turned me into a rose. A red rose in our own garden. And often I've watched you pass me by, without so much as a glance. But listen now, for I begged and I pleaded, and I begged and I pleaded, and at last they gave me a chance. Tomorrow morning, if you can pick me out from all the other roses, I can come back to you. But you only have one guess, and if you are wrong, I can never return.'

He brought her food, he brought her wine, and they began to think what they could do. Maybe... no, that wouldn't work. Perhaps... no that was no good either. How about... no, that was useless too. As soon as they thought of a watertight plan, they saw the holes in it. At last, as dawn was breaking, she had the perfect idea. But before she could tell him, she saw the sun rising, and straightaway she lost the power to speak, or the power to stay. He tried to stop her, but she ran out of the door. He hurried after, but he was too late. All he could see, in the early morning light, was row upon row upon row of beautiful blood red roses.

So now it's up to you, if you want a happy ending. How did he pick her out, from all the other roses? Or didn't he?

Helen East

WISHES AND SURPRISES

Washing-up water

Some time ago, but not so long ago, before taps brought water into your own house, there was an old farmer who lived by himself. 'The old boy', the neighbours called him when they talked about him.

'Ay, he's a funny old boy,' They would say. And he was. But he certainly knew how to look after himself. For instance, every day as regular as clockwork, this old boy would wash up his dishes. Sometimes he had pwtsh[1] for dinner (that's mashed potatoes with butter and milk). Sometimes he had bara tê[2] (that's bread in a basin with tea poured all over). But whatever he had, he would wash up his things as soon as he had finished, just like his mam had taught him to do.

This is how he did it. He poured the water into his kettle. He took the kettle to the Gegin Fawr[3]. (That was the name for the kitchen where he had his fire.) He put the kettle on the range (the range was the stove where he did his cooking) and when the water was boiling, he took it out to the Gegin Fach[4]. (That was the name for the little kitchen where he did his washing-up.) He poured the water into the bowl, put in some soap, picked up his rag and washed up his dirty dishes.

After he'd finished washing up, the old boy would throw away the water. But he couldn't tip it down the drain because there wasn't a drain in his sink. No. He picked up the bowl, carried it out of the Gegin Fach through the back door into the garden, straight down the path to the wall at the bottom. There, he lifted the bowl and tipped the water, slosh, straight into the field on the other side.

1. Pronounced 'pooch'

2. Pronounced 'bara tair' to rhyme with 'hair'

3. Pronounced 'gegin vowr'

4. Pronounced 'gegin varch' ('ch' as in 'loch')

Every day it was the same. And every day the washing-up water ended up in the field. Never once did he take it over to the cow shed to give to his cows (he gave them clean water to drink) and never once did he dream of taking the washing-up water to the vegetable garden at the side of his house. Which is why the leeks he grew looked very thin and weedy. They could have done with some water!

No. Every day the washing-up water ended up in the field, slosh, spot-on, in exactly the same place.

One day, this farmer had cawl for his dinner. That's a delicious kind of soup made with meat and potatoes and carrots and parsnips and swedes and onions and lots of green leeks. The old farmer looked at his leeks. 'Jiwcs[6],' he said. (He often talked to himself.) 'Pity they're not a bit bigger.'

But never mind, the cawl was delicious – though it was never as good as mam used to make it – and after he'd finished, the old boy went out to wash up his basin and spoon.

And on this day like on every other, he carried the dirty washing-up water to the bottom of the garden and tipped it into the field. But on this day something different happened. Something very surprising.

As soon as the water sloshed into the field, the farmer heard a voice.

'Drat you,' it said. 'That's enough of your water. Drat, drat, drat, drat, drat.'

The old farmer was highly surprised. A voice! Yet there was no-one around. He looked into the field. No-one. He looked behind him, no-one. There was no-one anywhere.

'And don't pretend it's not your fault! You're ruining my life!'

There it was again. The farmer couldn't believe it although he could hear it and it seemed to be coming from over the wall. He went close by the wall and looked over. No, at first sight he couldn't see a thing except for the grass and some flowers and weeds.

'Down here, drat you! Down here is the problem, not over there by where you're looking!'

The old man peered down and to his amazement, he saw a little man. The little man was standing close by the wall, looking up. He had a long grey beard and a little green cap, a little red buttoned-up jacket, black trousers, white socks and black buckled shoes. And he had a very cross look on his face.

'Who d'you think you are?' he was shouting.

The old farmer didn't know how to reply. 'What's all the fuss?' he said. 'What's wrong?'

'What's wrong?' the little man exploded. 'You come over this side and I'll show you what's wrong.'

5. Pronounced 'Jooks', an exclamation

It took the farmer, who had a stiff back, quite a long time to climb over the wall, especially since, as soon as his foot was over, the little man began shouting again.

'Not there, drat you, over here, or your great big foot will be the end of us all.'

When he finally got both feet on to the ground, the farmer had a good look round. Apart from the little man, he could see nothing at all unusual.

'Dear me!' he said 'You must be having me on. I can't see what all this fuss is about.'

With that, the little man walked towards his right boot – he really was very small – and started climbing on to it.

'Where d'you think you're going?' the farmer shouted. 'What d'you think you're doing?'

'You'll see,' replied the little man.

He was right. As soon as the little man got up on to his boot, the farmer saw a whole new world appearing at the bottom of the wall. A house and gardens, farm buildings and fields... everything was neatly laid out. But it was obvious that all was not well. The whole place was swimming with dirty washing-up water. Soapy water dripped off the roofs, soapy water swirled round the paths, soapy water was flooding the fields – and in the fields tiny cows and sheep were dripping with soapsuds too.

'Mari! Mari!' shouted the little man, turning towards the little house and nearly falling off the farmer's boot as he did so. 'I've got him here! I've got him at last!'

The farmer bent towards the house only to see a window flung open and a fist fly out.

'Shame on you! Shame on you!' shouted a furious voice. 'You better change your ways before we change our manners or you can expect some trouble from us. We're not going to put up with this any longer.'

What could the old farmer say? What could the old farmer do? He told the little man and his wife – for it was the little man's wife, Mari, whose fist he had seen – that he was ever so sorry for all the mess. He said he didn't mean it and he promised them faithfully that from that day on, he would change his ways. And he did.

From that day on, he never again tipped his washing-up water where he always used to. From then on, he took it to the vegetable garden at the side of his house and tipped it on to his leeks. Which is why, from then on, his leeks grew big and strong and juicy and his cawl got even more delicious than it used to be before.

'Nearly as good as Mam's,' the old boy started saying when he had cawl these days.

And every now and again, after that, he would take some cawl to the little people. First he would call out loud until the little man or his wife appeared. Then he would lower the cawl in a tiny little pot at the end of some string. But, although he always saw one of them, he never saw their house and gardens again because, to be honest, he was a bit too stiff to climb over the wall. And unless he climbed over the wall, the little man couldn't stand on his boot. And unless the little man stood on his boot – well, you know what little people are like!

Mary Medlicott

The farmer and the unicorn

On the edge of Minchinhampton Common in Gloucestershire there lived a farmer who was poor and had always been poor. That was bad enough. But as well as that, his old parents lived with him and his mother was blind and had been so for many a year. That was bad enough. But as well as that, the farmer and his wife longed for children, but no baby had ever been born to them. That was bad enough, but as well as that, one year the harvest failed, and the time came, one winter's day, when his wife said to him, 'There's no more food in the larder. There's no more money to buy food with.'

'Well,' said the farmer, 'there's one thing I can do so we don't starve. I'll take my gun, and go out on the hill, and I'll shoot something for our pot.'

So he took his gun and went out, and went up the hill, and down the hill, and up the hill, and down the hill, and up the hill, and down the hill. But he didn't see a hare, or a rabbit, or a pheasant, or a partridge, or even a pigeon that he could shoot for his pot. It began to get late, and he was cold, tired and hungry.

Just at the time between daylight and nightdark, he came to a tree with branches long and low so he couldn't see what was round the other side. As he came round it, he found himself face to face with a snow-white unicorn – that creature of whom many have spoken, but few indeed have seen.

For one moment, for two moments, he stood motionless with wonder. But then he thought, 'This may be the rarest of all rare beasts, but a beast it is and it would fill our pot!'

And he raised his gun and aimed. As he looked along the sites of his gun he found that he was looking straight into the eye of the unicorn. In that eye, he saw things. He saw worlds beyond the world, he saw years and centuries beyond this year, and he knew that this creature was a creature so alive it made all other creatures seem half dead. He also knew that he could not kill it. He began to lower the gun, and as he did so there came a voice upon the frosty night air.

'For letting me live,' it said, 'you have one wish and one wish only. Wish well.'

It was the voice of the unicorn. In the next moment it turned and galloped up the hill, and in the moment after that it was gone, never to be seen again.

When the farmer came home, he told his family what had happened. His father spoke first, 'My son, haven't we always been poor? Wish for money!'

But then his old mother spoke up, 'My son, many a day has passed since I saw the light of day or the faces of my loved ones. Wish for my sight to be returned!'

But then his wife spoke, 'My husband, how long have we wanted children? Wish that a baby be born to us!'

Well the farmer was so confused he almost wished he'd never been given the wish! One thing he knew, and that was that when you're given a wish, you can't use it to wish for more wishes. So he got up and went outside again, and spent a long time standing in his farmyard and looking up at the stars.

In the house everyone waited to hear what he would decide. Then at long last, the door opened and in he came. As they all listened anxiously, he spoke these words:

'I wish for my mother to be looking at my baby, asleep in a cradle made all of gold....'

And so it was.

Kelvin Hall

The stone

Just outside the town there was a field with a huge stone in the middle. This stone was about as big as a car. It was covered in grey lichen and green moss. In the summer the children would climb on to its back and play at jumping. They used it for a base from which to play games.

One summer, a girl called Tula climbed the stone and noticed that there were marks carved into the rock face. No-one had really seen these before because of the moss and lichen. The marks were not very clear but she went home and got some paper. She climbed back on to the rock and began to draw out what she thought the words said. It took her a long time as some of the letters had been almost worn away.

The words said:

*Turn me over
to your advantage.*

She ran home and told her Mum and Dad. Her Dad swore her to secrecy. No one else must know about this, he said. Because it must surely mean that somebody had once buried something beneath the stone. Perhaps it was gold. Maybe it was silver. Who knows what it could be. And no-one would ever know unless they turned the stone over to find out for themselves.

So late that night Tula's Dad and her three Uncles set out to turn over the great stone. They took torches to light their way and great tree branches to help push the stone over. It seemed as if they would struggle all night. Their muscles ached and sweat frosted their brows. At times they thought that the great stone would be stuck forever. But the thought of what might lie beneath drove them onwards. Till with one great heave the stone groaned and rolled over. And the four men stared into a dark space on the ground.

They flashed their torches on to the earth but all they could see were earthworms and beetles. Till Uncle Jeera said, 'Look, there are words written on this side of the rock too.'

And they all read:

Thank you for rolling me over.
I was fed up with lying
on the other side.

Pie Corbett

Kanai's betel nut

Appoh[1]! Well then...
Once,
long ago,
when Rajas ruled,
and stories were true – you remember that time, eh? No-no, you wouldn't.... Well... in that time, there lived a poor, tired, old man called Kanai[2]. He was one of the Raja's gardeners. Do you think he liked it, eh? No-no, he didn't. From morning till night, he had to hurry and scurry, here, there and everywhere, tending fountains and flowers and fine fruits of all sorts. He never got a moment's peace. And even though he was surrounded by luxury and riches, he was often cold and hungry himself. In fact, the only thing Kanai did have was a big family, and do you think that made life easy, eh? No-no, it certainly didn't. Too many mouths to feed, and backs to clothe, and worries to weigh on his poor old head, that's what he thought. Poor old Kanai, all he ever wished for was a little rest in the shade, with a little betel nut to chew and a little time to himself to enjoy it. Would you think that was too much to ask, eh? No-no, surely not. But it seemed it was.

Well... things can go from bad to worse. One morning – early, early, even the birds were still asleep, Kanai came into work and what did he see? Oh-oh, it was terrible. Trees were trampled, paths smashed, water splashed all over the place. And right in the middle of the finest flower bed was a simply enormous footprint. Just one. Nothing leading to it. Nothing leading from it. It just didn't seem to make sense. No-no, it certainly didn't.

Well... there wasn't time to sit and wonder. Kanai set to work as hard and fast as he could clearing up all the mess. By the end of the day he had almost finished. But how could he go home? Maybe what-ever-it-was would come back and do the same thing again. No-no, he couldn't have that. He would have to wait and watch and see what it was. Maybe he could catch it. So long as it wasn't too big! Was he scared, eh? Mmm-yes, of course he was!

Still... he waited.

At last he heard a noise. A TREMENDOUS noise. It sounded like trumpets, it sounded like thunder, it sounded like elephants – and so it was! A simply stupendous elephant covered in silk and silver bells was floating down from the sky. It landed gracefully on one foot, right in the

1. 'Appoh!' is a phonetic rendition of a colloquial expression used in the southern Indian state of Kerala, which can be roughly translated as 'Well then', 'Now then' or 'OK'
2. Pronounced 'Kuni'

middle of the flower bed, and at once began to tear up trees and gobble up prize plants all around.

Kanai was amazed, but maybe not quite as you might have been. For he knew straight away that this was no ordinary elephant. This was Airavatha[3], the elephant that belonged to the Raja of the Gods himself, Lord Indra. It must have come down from the kingdom of the sky, to see what the world below was like.

'Ooh-oh!' thought Kanai. 'If only I too could move between worlds. If only I could see that heavenly sky kingdom, I would never wish for more!'

Then, suddenly a clever idea struck him. He rushed out from his hiding place and grabbed hold of the elephant's tail. The elephant, surprised, tried to shake itself free, but Kanai held on firmly. The elephant tried to run away, but still Kanai clung on. Finally the elephant, thoroughly upset, decided to escape back home. With a WHOOSH it took off into the sky, higher, higher, higher. And Kanai, still clutching its tail, went with it.

Higher, higher, higher. Beyond the tallest tree tops, beyond the clouds, beyond sight of earth. Kanai didn't dare look down, or up. He closed his eyes and gritted his teeth. Higher, higher, higher.

Then, just as he felt he couldn't hold on any longer, he suddenly smelt flowers and fruit and delicious spices and heard the clatter and clamour of people and pots and pans... and felt solid ground beneath his feet at last.

'I must be in Heaven,' he thought.

And so he was. What's more, he'd arrived on market day. Can you imagine what it was like, eh? Aah-ha, it was out of this world. Everything was so bright and beautiful and BIG. Ten times better than anything down here. You know how big the oranges were, eh? The size of my fist? No-no, they were as big as my head! And the jewellery, eh? Nose-rings and earrings that would fit round your neck; finger rings you could wrap round your waist. And the sweets and cakes and biscuits? They were THIS big. And the spicy snacks and nuts? They were THAT big. Oh, oh, oh, so do you know how big the heavenly betel nuts were? Kanai could not believe his eyes! Down here you could pop one in your mouth. Up there you could hardly hold one in your arms! Do you think Kanai could resist, eh? No-no, he had to buy one, even though it cost him all the money he had.

Well, there was so much to see, and hear, and enjoy, the time flew past, and it was only when he saw Airavatha hurrying past, that Kanai remembered his home. He must have been gone for hours. Surely his

3. Pronounced 'Aravata'

family would be worried. Carefully clutching his betel nut, he took hold of the elephant's tail again. As luck would have it, Airavatha was just on his way down below for another rampage, so in no time at all Kanai was safely back in the Raja's garden.

Well, can you imagine what happened when Kanai got home with his story? At first they could hardly believe him, but when he showed them the betel nut OOH AAH! they had to, then, didn't they! But do you think Kanai's wife was pleased when she saw what he'd got from the heavenly kingdom. No-no, she was NOT!

'Lazing around, chewing and spitting, that's all you ever dream of!' she cried. 'You and your wretched betel nut – that's all you thought of, wasn't it? What about me? What about the children? Can we eat betel nut? Can we wear betel nut? Can we sleep on betel nut? No, we can NOT! Oh you stupid selfish senseless sluggard, I wish I'd never married you!'

Ooh-oh. Kanai felt awful. He just hadn't thought. But now he did. He thought and thought and then – he had a good idea.

'Come and meet me at the garden tonight,' he said to his wife. 'When the elephant comes, we can both hold on to its tail and go up to the sky, and you can buy anything you like up there.'

Well of course Kanai's wife was delighted; straight away she dried her eyes, and began to make a shopping list.

A little later, her mother came round. Kanai's wife had meant to keep her plan a secret, but it isn't fair to keep good fortune to yourself, is it? No-no, of course not. So she told her mother, but asked her to keep it quiet. Now the mother didn't mean to, but later she met a friend. You should share things with friends, shouldn't you? Yes, yes, of course. . . but then the friend told her husband... and so the news went round from mouth to mouth and house to house until in the end the whole village knew.

So that night, Kanai, waiting for his wife, got a bit of a shock. In dribs and drabs and droves the entire village arrived, giggling and gossiping and jiggling their money, all ready for the heavenly market. Even the beggar from outside the temple was there.

'Very well,' said Kanai, 'if we've all got to go, we'll have to be organised. Let's make a human chain. I'll hold the elephant's tail, my wife can hang on to me, her mother can hang on to her, and so on all down the line. But hurry up, and hold tight!'

Everyone rushed to get in line, just in time, for at that moment they heard the great sound and saw the great sight of Airavatha hurtling down from the sky. This time Kanai hardly even let him land before reaching out and grabbing his tail. Airavatha was horrified – the thing on his tail seemed to be bigger and heavier than before.

Up he WHOOSHED, up and away, as fast as he could. And after him, with him, clinging on for dear life, went the long line of people, shaking and swinging and swaying from side to side. Right on the very end came the beggar. Do you think he was enjoying himself? Nah-noo, he was feeling rather sick.

Higher and higher they went, and higher and higher and higher still. And the poor beggar, he felt worse and worse. He began to wonder whether heaven was really worth all this bother. After all, how big was the betel nut that Kanai had brought back? The beggar had never seen it himself. Maybe it wasn't so big after all. He asked the person next to him, but they hadn't seen it either. How big WAS the nut? The question passed from person to person. How big was the NUT? Everyone was getting worried. How BIG was the nut? The question travelled up the line. At last it came to Kanai.

'Don't worry!' he called. 'It really was huge. How huge? Well, at least THIS big' – and he held out his hands to show.

Oh-ooh! He quite forgot he was holding the elephant's tail. And when he let go? Well, down they all fell. Down down down to earth with a bump. And that was the end of that trip to heaven.

And that's the end of this story too.

Do you think it's true, eh?

Aah-ha, well that's up to you.

Helen East

The nixie of the pond

Once there was a miller, who lived in his house with his wife. They had money and property and it seemed that their wealth increased from year to year. But then, as it goes in the affairs of the world, as their wealth had increased, so it began to decrease and soon they were so poor that they could hardly call the mill their own.

The miller began to worry and fret, and at night he would lie awake in his bed, tossing and turning. One night, unable to sleep, he got up before dawn and went for a walk.

He was crossing the dam of the millpond just as dawn was breaking, when he heard a sound in the pond. Turning around, he saw a beautiful woman rising out of the water, her long hair falling over her shoulders. The miller's heart froze! He knew that this was the nixie of the pond, but he didn't know whether to run or stay. But she called him by name and spoke so softly that he decided to stay.

'Miller,' said the nixie, 'why are you so sad?'

'Well, to tell you the truth,' said the miller, 'business is bad, I've got no money, I don't know what to do.'

The nixie laughed and said, 'Oh, Miller, there's no need to worry. If you will give me what has just been born in your house, I promise you that you will be rich again, richer than you have ever been.'

'What has just been born in my house?' thought the miller. 'Why, that's sure to be a kitten or a puppy.'

'All right,' he said to the nixie. 'If you make me rich again, you can have what has just been born in my house.'

'It is done,' said the nixie. 'Remember your promise to me.'

And laughing, she disappeared under the water.

The miller went home with a light heart but, as he got to his house, the maid came out to meet him and said, 'Congratulations, sir! Your wife has just given birth to a beautiful boy.'

'What!' gasped the miller, and then he knew that the laughing nixie had tricked him.

He went upstairs to see his wife and she said, 'What's wrong? Look at our baby. Isn't he beautiful?'

Then the miller told her of the nixie and his bargain with her and neither his wife nor any of the people that came to the christening could offer any advice.

From that day on, the miller and his wife got richer and richer. It seemed that their treasure chests filled themselves overnight. But no matter how rich he got, he knew no peace for he could never forget his promise to the nixie. He kept himself well away from the millpond, lest he should see the nixie and as he grew, he told his son never, ever to go near the pond.

The years passed with no sign of the nixie. The boy grew and became a young man and he left the village and became apprenticed to a hunter. When his apprenticeship was done, he returned to the village, fell in love and married.

Now one day he was out hunting in the forest, when he saw a deer. He started to chase it, but no matter how fast he ran, he could never quite catch up with it. Finally it ran out of the forest, into open country. The hunter chased after it and eventually managed to get close enough to kill it. Then he skinned it and when that was done, he wanted to wash his hands in the nearest water – the millpond!

The moment his hands touched the water the laughing nixie appeared, took hold of him and dragged him under the water.

When he didn't return home that evening, his wife began to worry and set out in search of him. When she found his hunting bag and knife close to the millpond, she knew at once what had happened, for he had often told her of the nixie. She walked around and around the pond, calling his name and cursing the nixie, but the pond lay still and silent and all that looked back at her was the face of the half moon, reflected in the water.

Eventually, exhausted, she fell asleep and as she slept she had a dream. In her dream, she saw herself climbing a nearby mountain and as she climbed it, the brambles snagged her clothing, the wind howled and the rain poured down. But when she got to the top, the sun came out and she saw a little hut in a valley. She went to the hut and opened the door. Inside there was an old, old woman who looked up and smiled at her.

When she awoke, the sun was already high in the sky and she knew that she must follow her dream. So she went to the mountain and began to climb it and it was just as in her dream. The brambles snagged at her clothing, the rain poured down and the wind howled. But when she got to the top, the sun came out and she saw the little hut in the valley. She went up to it, opened the door and there was the old woman, smiling at her.

'Well, well,' said the old woman. 'Your troubles must be great indeed for you to visit me here. Tell me what the matter is.'

And the young woman told the old woman all about the nixie.

When she had finished her story, the old woman said, 'Well, well, don't worry. When next the moon is full, take this golden comb and go and sit beside the pond and comb your hair with it. And when you are done, place the comb beside the pond and you will see what you will see.'

So the young woman thanked the old woman and took the golden comb and when next the moon was full she went and sat beside the pond and combed her hair with it. And when she was done, she placed the comb beside the pond and, a moment after that, a wave ran across the pond, took hold of the comb and pulled it under the water. And a moment after that, her husband's head rose up out of the water and he looked longingly at her. But then he was pulled back under the water.

'Oh, what good is this?' she cried. 'To see his face only to lose him again.'

And again she fell asleep, and again she dreamed of the old woman.

The next day she climbed the mountain and went to the little hut and told the old woman what had happened.

When the old woman had heard the story, she said, 'Well, well, don't worry. When the moon is full, take this golden flute and go and sit beside the pond and play on it. And when you are done, place the flute beside the pond and you will see what you will see.'

So the young woman thanked the old woman and when next the moon was full, she sat beside the pond and played on the golden flute. And when she was done, she placed it beside the pond and, a moment after that, a wave ran across the pond, took hold of the flute and pulled it under the water.

A moment after that, her husband's head and the top of his body rose out of the pond and he reached out his arms towards her. But then he was pulled back under the water.

'Oh, what good is this?' cried the young woman.

And again she fell asleep and again she dreamed of the old woman. The next day she climbed the mountain, went to the hut and told the old woman what had happened.

When she had heard the story, the old woman said, 'Well, well, don't worry. When next the moon is full, take this golden spinning wheel and go and sit beside the pond and spin on it without stopping, until the spindle is full. Then place it beside the pond and you will see what you will see.'

So when next the moon was full, the young woman went and sat beside the pond and spun on the golden spinning wheel until the spindle was full. Then she placed it beside the pond and, a moment later, a wave ran across the pond, took hold of it and pulled it under the water. And a moment after that, her husband appeared on a waterspout in the middle of the pond, and he leapt from the waterspout on to the bank and they caught each other by the hand and started to run away from the pond.

But as they were running, they heard the sound of water behind them and, turning around, they saw a great wall of water rushing towards them, sent by the nixie to destroy them. And, in her fear, the young woman called out to the old woman for help and in an instant they were changed, he into a frog and she into a toad.

Now the water couldn't destroy them, but it carried them away and away and away, to far distant lands and it separated them. When the water receded, they took back their own forms, but neither had any memory of the other.

To make their livings, they both became shepherds, and for many years they each wandered alone with their flocks until, one spring, they both came to the same valley and although they didn't recognise one another, they took pleasure in each other's company and they let their flocks run together.

And it happened that one evening, when the full moon was shining bright, he took out the golden flute and played a beautiful but mournful tune on it. And when he looked at her, she was crying.

'Why are you crying?' he asked.

'Because,' she replied, 'because the last time I heard that flute I saw the face of my beloved.'

And at her words, it seemed that the scales fell from their eyes and they recognised each other and they ran together and embraced. And there's no need to ask if they were happy.

Tim Bowley

The silver bell

Long ago, at Erritsø[1], there was a rich farmer who had two sons. When the time came for him to die, he called the sons to him.

'As is the custom, I am leaving the farm and all my money to you, my eldest son,' he said. 'But I want you to promise me that you will look after your brother.'

Of course the eldest promised, but as soon as his father was dead, he showed his true colours. He gave his young brother neither work nor money, and as for lodgings, all the poor lad got was a tumble-down pigsty away on the hill. It had a hole in the roof, a rickety floor and it smelt terrible.

'But it's good enough for him,' said the eldest brother. 'I only promised to look after him, I didn't say I'd do it well.'

The young boy didn't complain. He cleaned up the place, he mended the roof, and he tried to fix the rickety paving stones. Apart from that, he scraped a living doing odds and ends for anyone who took pity on him.

But there was one thing that did trouble the boy. The same thing bothered most of the people round about. You see, in those days there was no church at Erritsø. People had to travel miles for Christmas and christenings and weddings and funerals, and most ordinary Sundays they

1. Pronounced 'Erritseugh'

didn't manage to get to church at all, as it was just too far away. But no one had the money or the land to build a church. Except the rich brother, of course, and he wasn't about to spend his money on that – oh no!

One day they were talking about it, and complaining a bit too, down at the local tavern.

'You know where I'd love to see a church,' the young brother said. 'Up on the hill, where my pigsty is! If I had the money, I swear I'd build one there.'

It just so happened that his older brother overheard him. He'd been drinking rather heavily, and the thought of his penniless little brother building a church struck him as quite hilarious.

'You build that church,' he chortled, 'and I swear before all this company, that I'll melt down my silver – every last bit of it – to make your church a bell. Ha! Ha! Ha!'

Now maybe it was because of that talk, or maybe it wasn't, but that night the young brother had a very vivid dream. He dreamed a hand came shaking his shoulder, and a voice cried in his ear, 'Get up and go to the bridge across the river. There you'll find gold a-plenty for the church.'

The voice stayed in his mind the next day. But after all, it was only a dream. The river was a good few miles away, and the bridge as many miles again beyond that. He couldn't spare time and trouble to go so far on such a wild goose chase.

But the next night the dream came again. This time the hand shook him harder, and the voice cried louder, 'Why don't you listen! Get up and go....'

He nearly did take notice, this time, but then he thought, 'Why be such a fool? It's on my mind, that's all, that's why it's in my dreams.'

On the third night the dream came again. This time the hand nearly pulled him out of bed, and the voice was angry, shouting. This time he believed it. He got up, and before it was even light, he made his way to the bridge.

He arrived just as dawn was breaking, and with the first rays of sunshine he eagerly looked for the gold. There was nothing there. Just a plain wooden bridge across the river. Still he waited hopefully. Something would come, something would happen. He waited all day. He saw nothing and no one, except for a soldier, who rode by on his horse and waved his hand. The poor boy was cold and hungry, and he felt a complete fool. He'd wasted a day for nothing. But as he turned to go, he thought, 'The dream came three times, after all. Maybe tomorrow?'

So the next day he waited again. The day seemed even longer. What happened? Nothing and no one, except the soldier again. This time he stopped to call a greeting before galloping past. Now the boy was colder and hungrier too. 'Still,' he thought, 'what's to lose? I might as well try one last time tomorrow.'

So the third day he waited again. The day seemed even longer. What happened? Nothing. Towards evening the soldier came past again. This time he reined his horse in and stopped. 'I must ask you,' he said. 'What are you doing here? I've passed you every day, you're always here, and yet you don't seem to be doing anything. Please tell me, why are you here?'

You can guess how foolish the poor boy felt. All the same, he told him. He'd had a dream he'd find a fortune at the bridge. And so he'd come, but he'd got nothing. At least the soldier got a laugh out of it. He laughed until the tears ran down his face.

'Chasing dreams? Dreams of fortunes?' he cried. 'No wonder you're so thin and ragged looking! You're living on moonbeams, my lad. You'll never get anywhere like that! Did I get where I am today listening to dreams? Of course not. They're just wishful thinking, that's all. As a matter of fact, I had a good one myself, just the other night. Now what happened? – Oh yes. I was in this little hut – smelt pretty awful, must have been a pigsty or something. The floor was paved, but all uneven. For some reason I pulled up the centre stone, and started digging under it. And what did I find but a load of gold! That was a good dream, that was! Pity it wasn't real.'

The young brother listened politely. After a while he began to smile a little. He even began to hope a little. When the soldier had gone, he ran home and found a spade. He went into his pigsty-hut and lifted up the central paving stone. Then he began to dig. And what do you think? His spade struck iron. It was a box with a lock, a money chest, and it was filled to the brim with gold.

So that, they say, is how Erritsø got its church, and it's still standing to this day. As for the bell – well, when the elder brother saw the work beginning, he knew the village would hold him to his word. Even though he had meant it as a joke, it seemed the laugh was on him now. But the sight of all his silver being melted down to make a bell was more than he could bear. It is said his heart burst with rage, and he died on the spot.

So the younger brother got the farm too, as well as the church with the silver bell. And every time he heard it chime, he was glad that he'd gone chasing his dreams.

Helen East

Two furious red eyes

Danny and Tracy were twins. But before you get the idea that being twins made them able to guess what each other was thinking, and all that sort of stuff you normally read in stories, you've got to understand that they were totally different.

'Just like chalk and cheese,' said their mum to her friends, and breakfast time on the day this story begins will show you just what she meant.

It was Friday morning, half past eight and nearly time to leave for school. Danny was standing at the mirror combing his hair and checking that his tie was straight. Dad was in a flap.

'For heaven's sake, Tracy! Get down here and have some breakfast...

NOW!' he shouted up the stairs, then waited to hear the bump, bump of her footsteps overhead before returning to tidy up the kitchen.

'Check your room before you leave for school please, Danny. Your mum won't want to have to clear up your mess after the week she's had at work, and I'm starting nights tomorrow.'

Danny picked up the tea-towel and started drying up the breakfast things. 'It's OK, Dad. I got up early to do it, I know what it's like when Mum's had parents' evenings at school!'

The kitchen door bumped open and Tracy staggered into the kitchen, collapsed on to a stool and began pouring the cornflakes.

'Any tea in the pot?' she asked.

'I don't believe it,' said Dad. 'Just what are you playing at?'

Tracy looked puzzled. 'What do you mean?'

'I mean, you can't seriously be thinking of going to school like that. Look at the state of those jeans, they're filthy. You don't look as if you've washed, and I doubt if your hair has seen a comb for a week, let alone felt one!'

'Oh come on, Dad....'

Danny slipped away leaving the voices behind him. He'd heard too many arguments like this before and didn't fancy getting involved. But he was worried about his parents. Now that Mum had gone back to teaching, and Dad was working shifts it meant that everyone had to do their bit to help keep the house running smoothly, and coming home to a clean and tidy house meant a lot to both mum and dad. Danny put his toothbrush back in the holder, switched off the bathroom light and opened his sister's bedroom door.

'Oh no!' he murmured under his breath and his eyes took in the chaos of the room. The bed lay unmade and next to it the bedside table had on it a collection of six dirty mugs, two of which were beginning to produce some rather interesting green fungus. A pile of clean washing lay crumpled on the desk next to a half-finished painting, while dirty clothes lay strewn across the floor tangled up with a game of Monopoly, biscuit crumbs and various pieces of Tracy's 'My Little Pony' collection.

'I've got to do something about this, and fast!'

In fact it was morning break before Danny got the chance to speak with his sister. 'Look, Tracy, you've got to do something about your room before Mum gets home tonight. She'll go mad if she sees it in the mess it's in now.'

'Don't be so bossy, Danny. It's my room, isn't it? I can do what I like.'

'Yes, but you know how fed up she gets, particularly when she's had a load of late night meetings.'

'That's not my fault. I didn't ask her to go back to work, did I?' And with that Tracy flounced off to join her best friend Baljeet looking for froglets at the edge of the school pond.

Danny stood and wondered. What next?

Lunch times, Danny sat with his best mates Kamaldeep and Tom. School dinners varied a lot, but today they were all feeling pleased.

'Great! Fish fingers and baked beans,' cheered Tom.

'And treacle sponge and custard for afters,' sighed Danny, happily.

As the three boys returned from the dining room hatch with their plates, Kamaldeep asked, 'Hey Tom, what was that you were listening to in the library this morning?'

'What? The story cassette, you mean?'

'Yeah. There were some strange sounds coming out from the headphones.'

Tom chuckled. 'That'll have been Old Marley's chains.'

'Old who?'

'Old Jacob Marley. He's a ghost, see. In this story, *A Christmas Carol*. Comes back in chains to warn his old mate Scrooge to change his ways; stop being so mean to people. It's really good, you ought to have a listen.'

Danny sat back, pushed his plate away and began to smile.

Danny had a chess match that evening and so didn't get home till after his sister and mother. As he walked through the front door he wished he'd been even later.

'I don't care whose room it is – it's like a pigsty and I have to look at it! Get upstairs and tidy it NOW!'

Tracy stamped upstairs, shouting, 'I'm going up, but I'm not doing anything!'

'Then don't expect to come down again tonight,' yelled Mum at Tracy's retreating figure, before she stormed into the kitchen to shout at Dad. 'Why didn't you make her do it this morning before she went to school? You know I can't bear coming back home to this sort of thing. It's just like nagging the kids at school only worse.'

Danny sighed. It was going to be one of those evenings. But if his plan worked....

Danny rolled over and lit up his watch. 00.34. He listened carefully in the darkness. Silence. Pushing back the duvet he swung out of bed and tiptoed across the carpet to his bedroom door. He opened the door a crack, and could just see the outline of the bookcase on the landing, and beyond that Tracy's bedroom door.

He moved back into the bedroom and felt for the sheet he had hidden under his bed. Draping it over his head and body, he picked up the torch and tiptoed down the landing hardly daring to breathe.

He looked down at the door handle, turned it slowly and moved into the inky blackness of Tracy's room. As he moved towards the bed he could hear her snoring gently.

Danny turned on the torch beneath the sheet, began to sway from side to side and moaned gently, 'Ooooh, Tracy. Beware. Ooooh.'

Slowly Tracy woke up, stretched, rubbed her eyes and turned towards Danny, 'Hello, so you've come back then, have you? It's great to have a ghost to play with at night.'

Then Tracy paused and peered into the darkness behind Danny.

'Oh, but there are **two** of you tonight. Who's your friend?'

Danny spun round and stared straight into two furious red eyes....

Hugh Protherough

GODS AND GODDESSES

The apples of Iduna

One day when the world was young a miracle happened. A boat sailed to the shores of Asgard, the land of the Gods, and a young man climbed out. He sang a song of such beauty that even the trees bent forwards to catch a snatch of the music. As his feet touched the ground, flowers sprung up; as his hands touched the bare rocks, streams of living water flowed. Then the earth rose up like a great shaggy beast and shook itself. Great crumbs of soil tumbled down and when the earth settled down again, a beautiful girl stood there holding a golden casket.

The Gods heard the sound of the music and ran to see who this stranger might be. They met the singer and the young girl at the foot of the bridge they called Bifrost. Odin clapped his hands and laughed, for the young man was his son Bragi who had come to sing and make music for the Gods.

'And this is the girl I will marry, Iduna.'

Everyone wanted to meet Iduna, and Odin was curious to know what she carried in her golden casket. But he was careful to ask what was inside, for like you and I he had heard stories of no good that could come of opening boxes....

'Inside this casket are the Apples of Youth,' said Iduna. 'If you should eat one you would feel the fire of youth in your veins. You would shake off any illness, broken bones would mend and you would feel as if you might live forever.'

'This is good news,' said Odin. 'For in our battles against the giants we need to keep up our strength, and apples such as these will make us virtually invincible. But what happens when we run out of apples, the casket cannot hold many?'

Iduna laughed, 'But the casket never empties itself. It will always be full.'

'Then it is a rare gift and we must guard it with care. If the giants were to catch hold of this we would soon find ourselves in trouble.'

And he was quite right. When the giants got to hear of the famous apples, they knew that here was a prize well worth their while in catching. So Iduna never left Asgard and as none of the giants had ever found their way into Asgard it seemed that the casket was safe enough.

Now this story really begins because Odin and his brother Hoenir decided to travel into the world to see how ordinary men and women lived. They had travelled many miles, over mountains, through rivers, beneath the forest trees, across great plains where only the wind sang and the jack rabbit played, when they met Loki. Loki the shapeshifter, the trickster with giants' blood in his veins.

'Let me come with you, Odin, so that I can show myself good enough to side with the Gods in their fight against the giants.'

In this way Loki fell in with Odin and Hoenir.

Many miles they travelled, until they came across a part of the country where there was little food, and for days they lived on the roots of trees and had to chew the sap from leaves and grass. Till one morning they caught an ox in a valley. They settled down by an oak tree and soon a fire was blazing. Sparks shot upwards and Loki began to roast a haunch of meat. When it seemed cooked they took it off the fire but the meat was still pink and hardly done at all. Loki shoved it back on to the fire. Hoenir stirred the embers and heat sizzled upwards. The ox skin seemed to spit and crackle. Half an hour later they pulled the meat off the spit and Odin sank his teeth into the flesh.

'Euch, it's still uncooked,' spluttered Odin, spitting out raw meat and blood.

They stared at each other and Loki poked at the fire again, throwing another branch on to the blaze. Sure enough the heat was true.

'Your ox meat will not cook unless I assist,' croaked a voice from above them.

They peered up into the branches of the tree and stared in amazement at the huge eagle that spoke to them.

'Let me share your meat with you and then it will roast,' said the great bird.

Loki glanced at Odin who nodded his head. So, Loki shoved the ox back on to the spit and began to turn it steadily. Soon the smell of roasting meat drifted from the fire. Fat dripped from the great beast and spat in spurts of flame.

As Loki pulled the meat from the blaze, the great eagle hopped forwards and snatched its share. Not content with both front and back legs it began to tear great chunks from the ox's side. Indeed there was soon very little left. At this Loki protested but the bird carried on tearing meat for itself. So, Loki roared at the bird. 'You've taken too much. Leave some for us!' But the bird carried on tearing gouts of flesh. So Loki seized a branch from the tree and in his anger began to beat at the bird. The eagle's eyes flashed a warning and it beat its wings. But Loki caught it a tremendous blow on its back. And there the branch seemed to stick fast. Loki was unable to let go of his end of the branch and the branch was stuck to the bird. So, as the bird began to fly low over the ground beating its great wings so that dust

rose up in a cloud, Loki was dragged along behind. His legs dashed against rocks and soon his skin was torn and blood smeared the earth.

'Put me down! I'll do anything, just put me down!' screamed Loki in pain. 'I'll give you the rest of the meat, you can have the whole ox, I don't care.'

'It is not the ox I want, fool. It is Iduna and her casket of apples,' screeched the bird as it dragged Loki through nettles, over thorny bushes, banging up the side of the rocky cliff.

'But I can't get that even if I wanted to. I am not yet accepted as a God. They'd never welcome me into Asgard.'

'In that case I will fly through the day and fly through the night till you are no more than rags of bones and your legs are bloody stumps. For I am a Storm Giant. My power is as great as the thunder that rolls across the skies and as sharp as the lightning that stabs the earth.'

On flew the eagle, till Loki could bear the pain no longer and he cried out, 'Stop! I will try to get Iduna and her casket, anything, only stop before I am battered to death.'

With these words, the eagle flew back to where Odin and Hoenir sat by the fire. It left Loki lying on the ground, bruised and panting. Of course, he did not dare let Odin know what had happened so he spun a story that the eagle had seized him for attacking it with the branch.

So they travelled on and Odin was so grateful for the help that Loki gave them that he found him a place to live near the great bridge of Bifrost when they returned from their travels. Here Loki lived remembering well his promise to the Storm Giant. When he met Iduna walking he seized the chance he had been waiting for.

'Iduna, I have found an apple tree that has fruit just like your apples. They shine like stars and are as red as sunset. Just the smell of them made me feel ten years younger.'

Iduna frowned for she had believed that only she possessed the apples of youth but her curiosity got the better of her. She promised to meet Loki the next day with her casket so they might compare the apples he had found.

But as Iduna wandered into the orchard the Storm Giant swooped out of the sky and seized her in its claws. She struggled and kicked but it was no good. Its claws bit deep into her skin and soon she was no more than a dot in the distance.

After many miles they landed at a castle high on the top of a towering mountain. Iduna fell to the ground. When she looked up the eagle had disappeared and standing in its place was a huge giant.

'I must have your apples,' he roared at Iduna, but she clutched the casket to her and shook her head.

'No, only I will open this casket.'

The giant's roars shuddered through the mountain but it was no good. The casket could not be opened. After many weeks the giant grew tired of waiting and set off to the sea to fish.

Soon Odin realised that the apples had been stolen. Iduna was nowhere to be seen. Already the Gods were feeling the strains of old age. Their skin had begun to wrinkle, some hobbled, others complained of backache. Even Thor's hair began to grow grey. So Odin called the gods together. But no one knew where Iduna had gone. In the end he decided to go and ask Loki if he could find her.

'Perhaps I can help to bring her back but such a task will be difficult. Besides which I could not bring her into Asgard as I am not one of the Gods.'

'Return with her and you may join us, Loki. But if you enter Asgard without Iduna and the golden casket then I shall crack you in half,' swore Odin.

So Loki told Odin to build a huge bonfire in the gates of Asgard and to make sure that the Gods were on the lookout for him at all times. This done, he took on the shape of a falcon and flew to where the Storm Giant held Iduna.

The bird alighted on the stone parapet at the very top of the castle. Iduna was stunned when it spoke.

'Grab the casket! I am here to save you.'

She folded her cloak to her and Loki changed her into a walnut. The falcon, Loki, grabbed the nut and a moment later they were flying up and the castle was way below them. Iduna closed her eyes as the wind rushed by. Far beneath them, the streams were like ribbons and the forests became vast stretches of green. Iduna felt dizzy with the height but the falcon's grip was quite steady.

Meanwhile, unknown to them, the Storm Giant had returned, stinking of fish. With a roar that shook the teeth in its skull, the Giant changed to its eagle form. With great wing beats, it drew closer, ever closer to the tiny falcon. With each beat of its wings dust flew up, bushes were torn from the ground, trees uprooted. From Asgard the Gods could see the gathering cloud. They waited till in the distance they could just make out the tiny falcon, swift as an arrow, plummeting down towards the walls of Asgard. Behind it, like a darkening cloud, the great eagle swooped.

As the falcon flew over the great gates, Odin threw a blazing torch into the fire that waited there unlit and flames rushed up into the air. The eagle flew at a terrible speed straight into the blaze and for a moment could not be seen. The falcon shot over the flames and into Asgard while the eagle's feathers blazed like a funeral torch. The Storm Giant tumbled into the burning fire, its wings crumpling. Soon only the stench of burnt flesh could be smelt.

When Odin looked up from the white centre of the fire he looked into Asgard. And there stood Loki with Iduna. In her hands she held the golden casket. And in the casket, the apples of youth.

Pie Corbett

Don't touch, Pandora

See this box? Now whatever you do, you mustn't open it. You mustn't look inside. Not even the tiniest peek. OK?

No? You want to know what I've got in my box?

Well, I guess you're just like the girl in my story.

Once, then, once when the Gods were squabbling, there lived a beautiful girl called Pandora. She was so beautiful that the stars seemed to shine in her eyes, that the moon seemed to smile from her lips, that the sun seemed to burn from her face.

Everyone liked Pandora and she was the happiest girl that I ever knew. Happy enough, that is, until she found a box. Now this box was made of sandalwood. The edges were brass and the lid had patterns made from ivory on it. The lock was in the shape of a heart. It was a very special sort of box.

It sat in a corner of the house. And Pandora was told that whatever happened she should not open the box. She must not even touch it. On no account was that box to be tampered with. Got it? Right.

But the more she was told not to go near the box, the more she wondered about it. But....

'Whatever happens, don't you dare go near that box,' she was told.

'I've told you before, keep away from that box,' she was told.

'I don't want to have to say it again, but do not go near that box, Pandora,' she was told.

Well, what would you have done?

Oh dear, yes, she grew curious. She began to wonder what might be inside the box. She had heard folk say that curiosity had killed the cat but she knew that was rubbish. She would only take one little look. Just a peek. No harm would come of it.

Now what might it contain? (*At this point the children might make some guesses.*) Perhaps it was something nice that they were saving up for her? Maybe it was a special present? Whatever it was had to be something very important. But....

'Oi, mind your own business,' she was told.

'Hands off that box,' she was told.

'I've told you before, get away from there,' she was told.

But the more she was told to leave the box alone, the more she wanted to look inside. And I guess that by now you're really beginning to wonder what might be in there. Well, perhaps a little look won't matter, Pandora thought to herself for the thousandth time. Her fingers itched whenever she saw the box. Perhaps it had bright jewels to wear in her hair. Perhaps it had gold coins. But....

'That box is out of bounds,' she was told.

'You go near that box and I'll skin you alive,' she was told.

'I thought I'd told you to leave that alone,' she was told.

Till, late one afternoon, Pandora found herself on her own. She tiptoed over to the box and felt its cold, smooth surface. She took the key from where it had been left and slipped it into the lock. She turned the key and paused. Then she opened the box.

What happened next took her quite by surprise. For inside this box all the unpleasant things of the world were trapped. That is why Pandora had been so happy. But now they swarmed out like bees. They buzzed angrily and she threw her arms up to protect her face. All the horrors that had been imprisoned escaped from Pandora's box and flew out into the world.

Out flew death, disease, disaster, tears, cruelty, mockery, jealousy, tidal waves, hurricanes, volcanoes, earthquakes, war, spite, malice, unkindness, spit, wounds, pus, pain, agony, the scream of a friend in pain, broken friendships, divorce, lost toys, broken bones, tiredness, car crashes, flu, colds, coughs, cancer, leukaemia, AIDS, the squeal of tyres, chalk on blackboards, boredom, being made fun of, cramped zoo cages, experiments on animals, polluted rivers, smoking, smacks, drugs, drunkenness, broken teeth, bruises, hurt feelings, sad memories, junk food, moving home, saying goodbye, chicken pox, injections, not being able to spell, dyslexia, being laughed at....

SLAM!

Just in time the lid crashed down.

'I told you not to do that, didn't I?'

Inside the box buzzed one last insect. Its wings shivered. It was an insect called Hope. Yes, only Hope remained in the box. Little did Pandora know that Hope was what the world would need now that she had let all these terrible things out. Yes, it would be Hope that would keep the world turning, turning.

Pie Corbett

Baucis and Philemon

Once upon a time there was a valley where people lived with everything they could wish for. A river ran along the valley which watered the ground and made it fertile and fish swam in it which fishermen caught and people ate. There were fields full of crops, corn and vegetables, watched by a scarecrow – a man made of straw standing in the middle of a field to frighten away the birds who might eat the corn. And there was sweet long grass and clover where the cows would graze and hay could be cut to make soft, warm stables for the animals. Houses had long gardens where flowers and cherry trees grew and there was lots of space where children could play.

You would think that people would be happy in that valley but they were not. Though they had so much they were greedy for more. They peeped from behind their net curtains to see if their neighbours were getting things that they were not and they built walls and grew hedges round their houses to keep others out. They locked their doors and put gates at their entrances. No, people were not very contented in that valley – except for two people, an old couple called Baucis and Philemon, who lived in a cottage on the hillside, away from the best land and the smoothest paths. They were poor but they loved each other and survived on little, without wanting what others had in the valley.

And the gods watched what went on, as the gods do. The gods knew that people were greedy and selfish but, to be sure, they decided to test out the people in the valley. One day, two gods, Jupiter and Mercury, dressed up like men, like travellers and, when the sun was setting over the mountains in the early evening, they set themselves down in that valley and opened the wooden gate which led them up the path to the very first house in the main street. Someone from within peeped out through the window and the net curtains trembled a little. They knocked and they knocked – knock! knock! – but no one came to the door. They went to the next house and knocked on the second door. Knock! Knock! This time the door opened and there was a cross-faced man with a frown on his brow and his mouth turned down at the corners.

'Well, what are you after?' he asked.

'We have travelled a long way,' the gods said, 'and we would be grateful for something to eat and a place to sleep.'

'You can't stay here,' said the man and he slammed the door with a bang.

They went to the third house and knocked – knock! knock! – and this time a woman answered but they didn't have time to say they wanted something to eat and somewhere to sleep. Before they could open their mouths she shouted, 'Be off with you! We want no strangers, no travellers, no beggars round here! We keep ourselves to ourselves. We've got no time for anyone who is not one of us. Be off!'

And so it was in every house. Sometimes the door was slammed. Sometimes words were thrown at them. And sometimes people smiled a crooked smile and said they were sorry. But every door was shut against them. No one offered them so much as a crust of bread or a garden shed to sleep in.

Just one house was left, a little cottage on the side of the mountain, smaller than all the other dwellings and all by itself. It was the cottage where Baucis and Philemon lived. Through the gathering darkness they could see the cherry trees waving their branches round the doorway. And there was a little pond beside the winding path which led to the cottage door and a fat white goose gobbled among the water weeds at its edge. The gods knocked on the door – knock! knock! Old Baucis shuffled to the door, opened it and peered round, her old eyes searching the faces of the strangers outside in the dim light.

'We have travelled a long way and would be grateful for something to eat and a place to sleep,' said Jupiter.

Baucis did not slam the door. She opened it wide and let them in. The old man found sticks to  liven up the fire and asked the strangers to seat themselves in the two wooden chairs at the fireside. Baucis prepared more vegetables to add to the stew pot and, while it was heating up on the fire, she cleaned the table top and sweetened it with mint leaves which she rubbed all over its surface before laying upon it wooden bowls and stone pots and drinking vessels. She put in a jug what little there was left of the wine she had made herself from the elderberries they had picked from the hedgerows a year ago. She hoped that there would be enough food and drink in their poor cottage to satisfy the strangers.

The two gods talked little while they ate but smiled at Baucis and Philemon throughout. The wine was poured but – miracle of miracles! – the old couple saw that the jug of wine never emptied! Though the drink was poured in every beaker more than once, the stone jug remained full, with bubbles glinting on its surface in the candlelight.

'Alas!' cried old Philemon. 'These strangers must be gods! Forgive us for the humble welcome you have received! Our poor food is not fit for gods! Wait! We will find something better!'

And with that he hurried as quickly as his old legs would take him to the door of their cottage, and out into the moonlit night he went, thinking to catch the goose to provide their guests with a better supper. The goose, who was a sort of pet and a watchdog for the old people, flopped and fluttered and hissed with surprise and fear. It fled from Philemon's grasp and the old man chased it hither and thither under the cherry trees until finally the bird rushed through the open door into the cottage and cowered at the feet of the gods themselves. The old man, wheezing and puffing, followed after.

'Be at peace,' said Jupiter. 'You have given us more than enough. Now let us sleep. When morning comes you will be rewarded for your kindness.'

And so the night passed and morning came. The people in the cottage and in all the houses in the village woke up and looked out at the world. They had woken to the sound of a great wind that blew against their windows and against everything in the valley.

'O see!' said the god, Jupiter, to Baucis and Philemon. 'Look at the cherry trees! See how the wind of the gods shakes their branches and all the flowers that hang from their twigs!'

And the wet winds blew the bells wildly in the church steeple. They woke up the few who were still asleep and they rushed to their bedroom windows and watched the wind at work.

The wind quivered through the grass and pulled at the trees. It raced through the corn. It grabbed at the doors of sheds and tore at the nails which held them on. Windows were shaking and floors trembled. The swings and roundabouts in the children's park moved by themselves, as if invisible children played there.

Up above, great storm clouds bundled themselves together and the sky darkened. Down came the rain. Down came the rain in torrents. The pond shook its back and flashed its scales. The rain beat everything down except the river which rose higher and higher and scrambled up its banks and over the top, into the fields and on to the village street, while the little streams that ran down the mountain turned into pounding waterfalls which added to the waters in the valley.

'Get dressed! Gather your precious things! We must leave now!' the people cried to one another. And they left their houses and waded through the water and fled up into the mountains and away they went, away from that place of wind and storm and they never came back.

All that was left in the valley was a great lake. Fish swam through windows, in and out of people's houses. They darted among trees and played round the church steeple. Waves broke against the church bells which tolled a watery peel.

As for Baucis and Philemon, they watched in wonder until the rain stopped, the sun came out and a rainbow arched over the whole of the valley. Instead of living on a mountainside, they now found themselves beside a beautiful lake, their cottage just out of the spread waters' reach.

The gods gave them more than this as a reward for their goodness. They offered Baucis and Philemon the power to grant themselves one wish – just one wish they were given – whatever they most wanted in life would be theirs.

I am not sure what they wished for. What do you think two kind old folk like them would most want?

Some people say there are two trees in those parts, an oak and a lime, their branches twined together and their trunks touching. These trees are called Baucis and Philemon and some people say that their wish has something to do with those two trees, but I can't say.

Betty Rosen

The cyclops and the mermaid

This is the story of a cyclops. Now this cyclops was a giant of a monster. He was taller than trees and hairy as a goat. But worst of all was his eye. Yes, he had only one eye and that was in the centre of his head. He was so ugly that no one could bear to look at him without shuddering. But he wasn't much company anyway. For if stray boats ever came his way he would lie in wait till the sailors came ashore. Then he would reach out and grab a handful. And eat them for lunch.

All this and more till one day he fell in love. Yes, this huge lumbering creature fell in love with a beautiful young mermaid called Galatea. He would lie on the cliff tops and watch her swimming at the sea's edge collecting shells. He combed his hair with a great fir tree to improve his looks and took to bathing in the salt lakes to keep fresh. He rubbed his body in the scent of the olive trees that grew on the hillside.

Indeed, he fell so badly in love that he forgot about tending his sheep. He wandered the hillsides singing of his love. But the noise was so terrible that the birds would screech angrily from the treetops and the mermaids laughed.

The cyclops made up great poems about his love and would stand on the top of the cliffs reciting his verse in a booming voice. But none of this made Galatea fall in love with him. For she loved Acis, a young shepherd.

The cyclops felt his loneliness bite deeper than a knife blade. One night, as he stared into the flames of his fire, his eye weeping from the smoke and his sadness, he wondered how he could make her fall in love with him.

'Tomorrow,' he thought, 'yes, tomorrow, I'll go to the beach where she swims and I'll sing for her.'

So the next morning he rose early, combed his beard with his fingers and greased back his hair with the blood of a sheep. He tried to pick the fish scales from his finger nails with a tree trunk but gave up in the end. He picked the odd sheep bone from his teeth and spat them out as he made his way down to the beach. The morning sun rose as he strode across the sands. He felt the morning breeze lift his spirits and he broke into song. To his ears it was music – but the dolphins that wove the sea turned for another destination and the mermaids began to snigger.

The cyclops heard none of this and sang on of his great love. The words to his song were terrible

enough, but the sound of his voice was worse. It was like a great piece of chalk scraping across a blackboard, it was like the gears of a giant digger grating, it was like a sick dog howling in a well. It was awful.

Oh my love you are sweeter
than the tree tops
you are more beautiful
than the eyes of a cow
you are more lovely
than a mountain goat....

At this the mermaids burst out laughing. Unfortunately, the cyclops had paused for breath and he heard their laughter. He stopped and stared at them. And they scattered into the sea, their tails dipping and diving to escape his anger. Only Galatea was left running to where Acis stood at the edge of the beach. Together they stared up at the cyclops as he thundered up the sands towards them.

Seeing the two holding hands, the cyclops realised that Galatea loved the boy and not him. Stung with the pain of losing his loved one, he seized a rock and threw it in his hatred at the two lovers. The mermaid dived to one side but the rock crushed Acis.

Seeing blood ooze from under the rock, the cyclops shook his head and turned back towards his cave.

Galatea flopped on to the sands sobbing. If only she hadn't laughed at the cyclops maybe none of this would have happened. Through her tears she shouted into the morning sun to the Gods. She pleaded for Acis's life, as many had done before and many have done since. Who knows if any God was listening as she shouted.

'Save Acis, save him and take me instead.'

And as she screamed through her tears, she saw the blood from beneath the rock begin to flow like a stream. At first the stream swam thick and red but soon it cleared. It flowed stronger than ever across the beach and into the sea. Rain teemed down to swell the flow and the snows on the distant mountains melted. Galatea stared into the river for she thought that she heard a voice calling her. She thought that she could see the shape of Acis deep in the river.

And then into the river Galatea dived, the sun gleaming on her scales. For the shape of the person she loved most of all moved in the river. It was Acis, born again through her love into the shape of the river itself.

Pie Corbett

The spider's web

Now, who likes spiders? OK. Not so fast!

This is the story of a girl called Arachne who lived in Ancient Greece. When she was born, Arachne's parents were very poor – so poor that they did not always have enough food on the table, so poor that they often slept cold in the winter months. But as Arachne grew older, their fortunes began to change for Arachne had an amazing talent.

She could spin and weave anything you wished for – her skill was so great that soon the family became wealthy. People would travel miles to buy her cloth. As she wove, her fingers danced over the frame and brilliant patterns that stunned the eye appeared. She wove pictures that were so lifelike that some people swore that they came alive.

Now all this would have meant a happy life for Arachne and her family, but I'm afraid that her fame went to her head. You know how it is when people are good at things – some of them really let you know it. Well, Arachne was one of those. She bossed everyone around as if she owned the place – which unfortunately she did. In the end she became so boastful that she made a big mistake.

'You know, I think I must be the cleverest spinner there has ever been,' she said to her mother.

'If you say so,' replied her mother who by now was fed up with her daughter's boasting.

'In fact, I think that I can weave and spin better than anyone – even the Gods!'

Now as you can imagine, her mother didn't like to hear that sort of talk and told her so.

'Now, Arachne dear....'

'Don't you "Arachne dear" me,' snapped her daughter. 'I am more skilful than any of the Gods. Not one of them could weave a picture as beautifully as I. Look at all the ugly things they have put into the world. They can't be all that clever. After all, they made pigs and they are the ugliest of creatures. No, none of them could make beautiful pictures like I can.'

And with that Arachne tossed her head and strutted out of the room. Her mother sighed and hoped that no one else had heard such terrible boasting. But unfortunately, they had been overheard. Athene, the Goddess of war and wisdom, had heard what Arachne had said. Now Athene was rather proud of her own spinning and weaving and she wondered how good Arachne really was. So she disguised herself as an old woman and came to visit Arachne to see for herself. When she arrived Arachne was in full flow.

'You know, I think that some of the Gods should come for lessons from me. There's a lot they could learn. I gather Athene says she can spin. I bet I could outspin her any day.'

The old woman stepped forwards and said, 'Arachne, listen to an old woman. Perhaps you should be happy with being the greatest weaver on earth. But no one should place themselves above the Gods.'

'You silly old woman,' snapped Arachne. 'What would you know about spinning?'

'I may be old but with age can come the wisdom of experience. No one should ever think that they are better than the Gods.'

Arachne laughed scornfully, 'I am so talented at spinning that I sometimes wonder if I was the daughter of a God. Perhaps that is why I am so great. The Goddesses must be jealous of my skill. I bet Athene would never dare to test her skill against mine. She'd be too afraid of losing. Imagine the shame of that.'

'We shall see,' roared the old lady and at that moment there was a cascade of bright light. The old woman's ragged clothes disappeared, her grey hair and wrinkled skin faded. In a moment the Goddess Athene stood before them in her shimmering suit of armour. Most people would have been terrified, but Arachne just stared insolently. For now she knew that she could test her skill against the Goddess and she felt sure that she would win.

Most of the people who had been in the room had run off or fainted. Soon there was only the sound of weaving. It was a contest to see who would be the quickest and who could spin the most beautiful picture. They would stop as the sun rose.

All night they sat at their task, their fingers flickering across the frames as they tugged and pulled at the threads. The candlelight glowed, shadows danced and gradually a picture began to appear on each frame.

Beautiful colours threaded in and out. Arachne's mother stood by her  daughter, mesmerised by the beauty of the picture that emerged. There was a river of stunning blue with a huge, black bull standing beside a sheer white swan. The edges were threaded with purple and green grapes, gold and silver coins created patterns among red and yellow flowers and leaves of deep green. The colours shimmered. The picture showed the Gods at their worst behaviour as if Arachne was laughing at them. Her mother was transfixed by the beauty of the picture but in her heart she felt a deep fear for her daughter's insolence.

Athene's picture took the opposite view and showed the Gods at their best. She wove a special picture into each corner to act as a warning to Arachne. For each picture showed the fate of someone who had dared to challenge the Gods. But Arachne was beyond listening to any warning. Her eyes were held by the picture she was weaving and she put everything into it that her talent allowed.

As the sun rose, the two contestants stopped. Arachne's cheeks were flushed with the effort of spinning and her fingers were so sore that they bled. But when she pushed back the loom Athene was as fresh as when the contest had begun.

Athene stared at Arachne's picture and though she was loath to admit it, there was no doubt whose picture was better. Arachne's cloth truly did seem to be alive. The colours were so vibrant and the figures so lifelike that the picture held her gaze. Athene knew that she was looking at the work of a greater artist than she.

'It's better than yours,' hissed Arachne over her shoulder.

Which was the worst thing she could have done. Athene wheeled round and in a rage grabbed at her but Arachne stepped back and laughed.

'You thought you were so high and mighty but your picture shows you for what you are. Fat-thumbed and clumsy,' Arachne laughed at Athene.

But no sooner were these words out of her mouth than she realised that she had made a mistake.

Athene seized the spindle and smashed it down on to Arachne's head. Three times the blows fell. For a moment the Goddess paused and before she could strike another blow, Arachne's mother threw herself at Athene's feet.

'No, no, don't kill my daughter.'

And Athene smiled for she had thought of a most fitting way to settle the girl's arrogance. If she thought she was so fine at spinning then let her spin.

Athene seized the threads from the broken loom and wrapped them around Arachne's neck like a hangman's noose. Her mother gasped in fear as Athene hung Arachne from a rafter.

Arachne swung there, her eyes bulging as Athene cried, 'For your mother's sake you shall live. Your punishment for your vanity will be most fitting. A spinner you are and spinners your kind will always be.'

With these words she waved her hand at Arachne.

At that moment, Arachne's head seemed to shrink away, her hair falling to the ground like old silk. Her body began to bulge and swell. Her arms and legs disappeared scrunching up into her bulky shape. Eight of her skilful fingers stretched out into strange legs. Her body became a dark, blotchy colour. Hairs sprouted along the legs. Arachne's mother gasped at this terrible transformation, but Arachne could not speak. She hung in mid air, wheezing and puffing till her mouth seemed to melt and the skin closed together into dumb silence. Her eyes closed in a veil of skin. She could no longer speak. No longer sneer. No longer boast. But she could still spin....

Athene laughed. For her, the contest was over.

So if you see a spider today scuttling for safety, remember that Arachne was the first spider and she got that way because she dared to think that she was better than a God.

Pie Corbett

The death of Baldur

In Asgard there were two places where everyone was happy. One was the garden where the apples of Iduna grew. The other was where Baldur lived.

Ah, Baldur, the very sound of his name brings it all back. He was surely the most beautiful, the happiest, kindest and best loved of all the Gods. Did not the sun shine from his face? Did not his laughter shake the very core of the earth? Now, Baldur lived with his wife Nanna and their son in a palace called Breidablik.

In front of the palace there was a huge field where the young Gods would hold competitions and meet to practise different sports. There would be Heimdall who was the watchman of Asgard. His hearing was so good that it was said that he could hear the ears of wheat growing in the fields and the sound of the sunbeams drying up the summer earth. There too would linger Hodur, Baldur's brother. Poor Hodur had been born blind, and just as Baldur shone with the brightness of day, so Hodur's life was as dark as the night. Yet they loved each other.

Often these two would walk together, little knowing what was to happen to them and how their lives would move towards some terrible end. For this story really begins with a dream

In the dream there was an empty chair. And the chair was in Helheim where all things go when they die. In the dream there was the hand of death, but whose hand it was no one could see.

And this dream was dreamed by Freya's daughter, Hnossa, who woke crying one night. Her sobs were so loud and terrible that Baldur woke from his own dream and he too had been touched by an echo of the same place. He had seen himself walking with the dead into Helheim where an empty cup waited for him to drink from and where a bed lay waiting for him to take his last sleep.

When Odin heard of this he was worried for he knew that if Baldur was to die then it would mean the beginning of the end for the Gods. So he called his twin ravens to him and asked them to fly through the world to see if anyone or thing had heard such rumours.

So, like birds of the night the ravens flew, black as death themselves, their wings like the whispering of the wind. They listened for rumour, they listened for gossip, they listened to the dreams of women and men as they slept. They searched up and down the World Tree listening to the squirrels that ran at the tree's tips and to the snakes that writhed in the roots of the earth.

'What have you heard?' asked Odin.

The ravens settled and fluffed their beautiful feathers which shone with the sheen of good health. Their eyes of jet flashed as they croaked their message. They had heard that there was indeed an empty chair in Helheim. Odin shook his head at the news. Then and there he decided that he should travel into the very jaws of Helheim and find out for himself if it was true that Baldur was to die. Perhaps there would be a way in which he could stop the inevitable.

So Odin mounted his eight-legged horse Sleipnir and he rode towards Helheim. For three days and three nights he rode through darkness towards the land of the Dead. On the second night he paused at the top of a hill and listened. In the distance he could hear the sound of a dog howling – it was Garm, the hound of Helheim, on their scent. He spurred on Sleipnir who needed no further warning. All through the next day they rode with the sound of the dog baying and the scent of its last bloody meal on the wind. They rode through a wood of iron trees where the leaves were black and sharp as metal blades.

But at last Odin came to the gate of Helheim. Through the dark of the night he heard the sound of Garm, howling to keep out any who dared to try to escape. Odin sniffed the stench of rotten flesh and fresh blood. In the dark he could hear the heavy panting of the hound. Instead of entering Helheim he headed for the place where Völva the Prophetess lay in a long grave.

Odin clambered down from Sleipnir and cast a spell to force the Prophetess to rise from the dead and speak to him. The earth shuddered and the soil broke free as Völva rose up, and as she spoke even Odin's heart seemed to stand still.

Through her long dead lips she rasped, 'Who calls me back to life? Too long I have lain, my body washed by the rain, my bones eaten by the worms, shrouded by the snow, never warmed by the sun. Who dares to call me back?'

Odin cleared his throat but his mouth felt dry and he called out, 'I only want to know for whom the empty chair in Helheim is meant?'

Völva's body shuddered and through her lips of death she whispered back, 'There is mead for him to drink, there is a bed for his rest. It is Baldur they wait for. Now leave me.'

'I must know more,' cried Odin. 'Who will kill my son?'

'It will be Hodur,' hissed the witch.

As he rode back to Asgard, Odin turned over and over in his mind what he had learned. Perhaps there would be a way to save Baldur? How could it be that Hodur would kill his own brother whom he loved? But as he swung Sleipnir towards home he heard shouts of joy. Frigg, his wife, came to meet him, her eyes shining.

'All is well,' she said. 'I have found a way to save Baldur. I have made everything – every creature, every metal, every rock, even the earth, the sky and the sea promise to do Baldur no harm. Every serpent, every poison, every illness, everything you could name has sworn to do no harm to Baldur. Our son is safe. Nothing could harm him now.'

She smiled at Odin and he threw back his head and laughed, as if he had not just journeyed into the hands of death itself. What a clever woman she was.

The Gods were delighted that Baldur was safe and they began a new game on the field in front of Baldur's palace. Baldur would stand out front and the Gods would use him for target practice, roaring with laughter as their axes bounced off him leaving not a mark, as their arrows glanced off his skin and their spears dropped to the earth.

But Loki watched from a distance. He watched as Thor flung his hammer at Baldur. The hammer that could shatter mountains bounced off Baldur and returned straight to Thor's hand. And as he watched, a terrible jealousy burned in him and his hatred smouldered. Loki longed to be rid of Baldur's smiling face. Indeed, it seemed to Loki that the more he hated Baldur, the happier Baldur became. But how could he strike at someone who was invincible? How could you kill someone who could gargle with poison and not feel a thing? How could you kill someone who could swallow a snake alive and not die from its deadly bite? How could you kill someone who could juggle with balls of fire and not even singe a hair?

So, in the dark of one night, Loki changed his shape into that of an old woman. He disguised himself as Groa, who had been pulling out of Thor's head splinters of rock that a giant had smashed into his skull. He went to call on Frigg, who was delighted to meet Groa, and asked her about the extraordinary game of the Gods.

'Why,' laughed Frigg, 'That is my son Baldur. All things on this earth have taken an oath never to harm him. See how swords bounce off his skin. Everyone is delighted, for Baldur will surely never come to harm and his fun and laughter will bring us happiness for ever.'

'How strange,' croaked the old lady. 'You mean there is nothing on this earth that can harm him?'

'That is right, even the rarest of diseases have taken an oath not to attack him.'

'Is there nothing at all then?' pressed the old lady.

'Well, there was a mistletoe plant that grows on an oak tree beyond Valhalla that I did not bother with. It was so young and did not even have a proper root,' replied Frigg.

'Ah, I'm sure you were right,' tutted the old woman, smiling between stubs of teeth.

No sooner had she left the palace than Loki returned to his own shape and made his way to find the mistletoe. He cut a sharp pointed spray of mistletoe and carved its tip into a dart. He breathed upon it and it became as hard as iron.

As Loki came to where the fun and games were happening he looked around wondering how he might kill Baldur. Standing on the edge of the group of Gods was Hodur, staring as ever at nothing, listening to the Gods shout and laugh.

'Why do you not join in?' asked Loki, though he knew only too well.

'I have nothing to throw and besides I could not see. I wouldn't want to hurt anyone by mistake,' replied Hodur.

'Don't worry,' whispered Loki. 'Take this dart and I will hold your hand to make sure that your throw is true.'

So Hodur pulled back his arm and threw the dart as hard as he could with a great shout of laughter. The dart pierced Baldur's skin and he took one stop forwards before falling down dead. The Gods rushed forwards to Baldur leaving blind Hodur standing on his own, not knowing what had happened, calling to his brother, 'How did that feel, Baldur?' and laughing.

But Baldur would never reply, not now.

Once again it was Frigg who thought of a possible plan to save Baldur. She called for a volunteer to ride down into Helheim to see if Hel would take a ransom in return for Baldur's life.

So it was that Hermod, Baldur's brother, rode on Sleipnir down to Helheim. He rode out of the darkness across a river that burned, where the flames curled up round a huge golden bridge. He rode past the maiden of death, Mogdud, and into the very place where the Queen of Death lived. There it was that he met Baldur and there it was that he met Hel and knelt before her.

'Baldur can only return to you if what you say is true. If all living creatures mourn his death then let them cry. If there is even one creature that does not cry for Baldur then he will stay with me.'

So it was that Odin sent messengers around the known world. It seemed as if Baldur would be saved and brought back from death. Every day came news that more and more creatures had spoken for Baldur and shed a tear for the God they dearly loved.

Till Hermod came upon a place high in the mountains where a large black crow stood on a crag. Hermod got down from his horse and called to the bird but it hopped over the rocks. So he followed it till he came to an old woman at the entrance of a dark cave. She was dressed in rags and her face was sharp and savage as the moment of Baldur's death.

'I will not cry for Baldur,' rasped the old hag. 'Let Hel keep what Hel holds.'

'But everyone has wept for the death of Baldur, everyone loved him,' cried Hermod.

'The only tears that I shall cry will be tears that are dry,' cackled the old woman and with that she hobbled back into the cave.

A moment later, as Hermod peered into the darkness, the huge crow flew out cawing, 'Let Hel keep what Hel holds....'

Hermod returned to Odin with the bad news. Odin realised that the only thing alive who would be pleased to see Baldur die would be Loki – perhaps he had taken the shape of the old hag and the crow.

So Baldur's body and his favourite possessions were placed on his ship, Ringhorn. Nanna came to see Baldur's body for the last time but she was so overcome by grief that she too died. So they placed the two lovers side by side. But the ship was so heavy that a giantess had to be sent for to launch it. She came riding on a wolf, snarling across the beach. She had snakes for a bridle and even the Gods stepped back for fear.

The Gods stood on the beach as the burning ship was pushed out on to the seas. As the flames licked higher and higher, they saw a shape in the midst of the boat, stooping over the dead body of Baldur. It was Odin whispering a final secret into his son's ear. As the Gods watched, the boat moved towards the horizon, a column of smoke spiralling into the sky.

And the final word that Odin had whispered was the first word that had been heard. In the beginning. Fate had whispered it into Odin's ear and even he did not know the meaning of it. It was the word that was perfect and held a story inside it. Like an apple seed might hold an orchard, it contained more than itself. It was the story of the moment beyond, when the world of dreams and the world of men end. It was the story of Hope.

Pie Corbett

Notes on individual stories

How music came to the world

Origin
Aztec.
Age range
Five upwards.
Time
Eight minutes.

This is the first story that I ever collected. I made notes on it when I first read it. It is an Aztec creation myth.

Pamela Marre

The power of the small

Origin
Jewish.
Age range
Four upwards.
Time
Three to four minutes.

This is a Jewish creation myth about people working together. I started telling it to the children who came to my house to play. It's a great favourite. I think they like it because it is about small things. Just because you are small doesn't mean that you are powerless.

Pamela Marre

Six suns (or how the cock got his comb)

Origin
Chinese.
Age range
Five to six years.
Time
Five minutes.

I was first told this Chinese creation story by a student from Hong Kong. Fortunately she spoke excellent English, otherwise I would have missed a wonderful story that I have retold many times.

Barrie Wade

The sun, the moon and the sea

Origin
West African.
Age range
Any age.
Time
Eight to ten minutes.

This is a creation story from West Africa and retells the story of the Great Flood. During the telling of this story, the audience takes on the role of the characters, thus becoming players and physically moving around a stage. I have adapted the original story to include the creatures and objects of the sea.

Sandra A. Agard

Tortoise and the party in the sky

Origin
West African.
Age range
Any age.
Time
Eight to ten minutes.

I have adapted this story to include suggestions from the audience as to how Tortoise gets to the party. The aeroplane remains one of my all-time favourite suggestions; this was said by a little girl sprawled on my lap during a telling whom I thought was asleep. I counteracted by saying that all flights were booked, much to her dismay!

Sandra A. Agard

The hazel stick

Origin
English.
Age range
Seven to nine years.
Time
Five minutes.

I found this story in a nineteenth century book of country superstitions, when I was researching tree folklore. It was only about three lines long, and seemed rather on the side of Adam... but, reading between the lines (as you sometimes have to when you make a story your own) I could see just how it must actually have been. And so I ended up with this version.

Helen East

The Man in the Moon

Origin
Siberian.
Age range
Four to seven years.
Time
Ten minutes.

I gathered this story when I was collecting folk tales among the native peoples of Siberia. I found this in 1975 where the Chukchi live on the Kamchatka peninsula. The peninsula juts out into the Pacific Ocean opposite Alaska.

James Riordan

The pitch lake

Origin
Trinidad.
Age range
Nine upwards.
Time
Ten to fifteen minutes.

The Carib Indians were the first real discoverers of the Caribbean. They believed in the Sky God, the Earth God and in Nature itself. I tell this story a lot because it looks at vanity, pride, selfishness and the importance of respecting our environment. Pitch Lake is a real place in Trinidad. This story is the only explanation as to how it got there.

Paula Sorhaindo

'You're a liar!'

Origin
Russian.
Age range
Nine to eleven years.
Time
Ten minutes.

I've drawn on Irish, Palestinian and Russian versions of this story here, as well as inventing several bits myself. But because I've drawn most heavily on the Russian version, I've called the hero Ivan. You can find the Russian version in Aleksandr Afanas'ev's *Russian Fairy Tales*, the Palestinian version in Inea Bushnaq's *Arab Folktales* (both published by Pantheon Books), and the Irish version in Robin Williamson's *The Craneskin Bag* (Canongate).

Hugh Lupton

Master of all masters

Origin
English.
Age range
Six upwards.
Time
Eight to ten minutes.

The sense of humour and word play in this tale is a typical feature of English narrative. It was first collected by Joseph Jacobs in his *English Fairy Tales*.

Pomme Clayton

The king who liked a good yarn

Origin
Russian.
Age range
Seven to ten years.
Time
Ten minutes.

I recall first reading this story many years ago although I can't remember where. I've altered it quite a lot (and indeed nearly always add and subtract details and episodes when I tell it). I usually tell it solo, but it has also been a great success with my friend and colleague Huw Thomas (musician, singer, and alternative comedian – the type that aren't funny) playing the part of the king, interpolating his comments as and when, which audiences of children have found very exciting.

Gerard Benson

Feathertoes

Origin
Iroquois.
Age range
Five upwards.
Time
Ten to twelve minutes.

I found this story sitting on a shelf in a London library, twiddling its thumbs and bursting to be told. My pleasure!

Tim Bowley

The king who lost his queen

Origin
English.
Age range
Eight upwards.
Time
Fifteen minutes.

This is the story of a king who does not value his family. It really is a warning as to what can happen if you do not care for your people. It also says something about the importance of being able to tell stories and make things up.

Pie Corbett

Peapods

Origin
English.

It was only a long time after I started telling this story that I began to wonder why I liked it. Then I remembered that my

Age range
Eight upwards.
Time
Fifteen minutes.

older brothers are twins. It is another story about the strength of family bonds.

Pie Corbett

The dragon of Filey Brig

This is a retelling of a traditional tale from Yorkshire.

Margaret Greaves

Origin
English.
Age range
Seven upwards.
Time
Five minutes.

Soap

I heard this story from the American storyteller Jim May when we swapped stories over lunch one day in The Hole in the Wall pub near Waterloo Station. He told me it was in Richard Chase's famous collection, *The Grandfather Tales* (Houghton Mifflin, 1948) which I have yet to see. I did find a version later in Norah Montgomerie's excellent book *To Read and To Tell* (Bodley Head, 1962), but that too has been out of print for many years. It's a great story for audience participation and the fun increases as they begin to anticipate what trouble the next refrain is likely to cause.

Tony Aylwin

Origin
American.
Age range
Eight upwards.
Time
Ten minutes.

The three sillies

A 'noodle' story of which there are many variations on this theme. This particular version originally came from Joseph Jacob's classic collection *English Fairy Tales*, but it has evolved and changed through years of telling it in primary schools.

Hugh Lupton

Origin
English.
Age range
Six to seven years.
Time
Six minutes.

Ivan Berenekov

This tale is probably my favourite of all European 'Fool' stories. There is something we can all warm to in Ivan, as his dogged inability to comprehend any level of reality but his own sweeps all before it.

Tim Bowley

Origin
Russian.
Age range
Five upwards.
Time
Twelve minutes.

The lion and the foolish traveller

Two pupils in a South London comprehensive told me this story. It is really an extended joke. Of course, it hinges around knowing about saying grace before eating.

Pie Corbett

Origin
African.
Age range
Eight upwards.
Time
Five minutes.

Archie's besom

This is a traditional story which Duncan tells to children of the upper primaries in Scotland, unless it is a school in the Highlands where Gaelic is the mother tongue. This particular transcription is of a recording made during a storytelling session at Carbost Primary on the Isle of Skye. The English is often close to Gaelic constructions, and is a style known as 'Highland English'. The story is fantastically humorous, and appeals to

Origin
Gaelic.
Age range
Any age.
Time
Fifteen minutes.

adults as well, especially at Hallowe'en time.

Duncan and Linda Williamson

The man in search of his luck

Origin
European.
Age range
Nine upwards.
Time
Ten minutes

I first heard this story from the French storyteller Abi Patrix. Versions of it occur all over Europe and the Middle East. Sometimes the searcher finds what he is looking for, sometimes he misses it completely.

Re-telling a story that you have heard is easier than re-telling a text. The storyteller's voice lives on in your ear. When re-telling a text, allow it to move away from the written word, and shape itself with the help of the audience.

Pomme Clayton

Pwyll and Rhiannon

Origin
Welsh.
Age range
Seven to eleven years.
Time
30 minutes.

This tale is from the eleventh century *Mabinogion*. The stories were old when they were written down and are thought to have originated in pre-Roman Celtic society. It seems to me, therefore, that they offer us something quintessentially British.

Kelvin Hall

Uncle Bouki's Wow

Origin
Haitian.
Age range
Five upwards.
Time
Eight minutes.

There are many stories told about Uncle Bouki. He is usually outwitted by Clever Dick. This tale was originally published in *Tales for Telling* by Leila Berg (Methuen).

Bella and the Bear

Origin
Russian.
Age range
Four to seven years.
Time
Ten minutes.

This is a popular Russian story. It has drifted around the Slavic communities. I found a version in Bulgaria last year. It is everywhere you find bears!

James Riordan

The farmer and the boggart

Origin
English.
Age range
Eight upwards.
Time
Twelve minutes.

This is an old English tale that I love telling because the girl is so clever in outwitting the boggart.

Hugh Protherough

Clever Mary and the stone soup

Origin
British.
Age range
Eight to eleven years.
Time
Ten to twelve minutes.

The story of *The Stone Soup* is one which is very common and very well known in Britain and beyond, and one which I have heard many times from many storytellers in as many different versions. Sometimes it is told as a trickster tale, sometimes as a sentimental tale and sometimes it is told as a comic tale – purely for laughs, but it was not until 1992 when I heard the story told as a jocular Jack Tale by a young lad at the Sidmouth Folk Festival, that I found the right vehicle for the version of the story *I* wanted to tell.

I had always been drawn to the story by its social message –

the idea of sharing with those who have little when we have plenty, because we never know when we might need help ourselves. So I decided to convey that through a Jack Tale, but a Jack Tale in which Jack himself plays little part. Instead Mary is the prime mover in the story, getting the better of a greedy farmer who, let's face it, gets no more than he deserves.

Mike Dunstan

The parrot's advice

Origin
Jewish.
Age range
Seven to eleven years.
Time
Four to five minutes.

This is a Yiddish story and an example of convoluted thinking. It's a practical joke; why keep things simple when you can complicate them just as easily?

Pamela Marre

Coyote the trickster

Origin
Native American.
Age range
Eight to eleven years.
Time
Fifteen minutes.

The Great Plains tribes tell many stories about Coyote. In this story he acts as a helper to the people, but his tricks bring trouble as often as they bring help. For more American Indian stories, *American Indian Myths and Legends* by Erdoes and Ortiz is a useful source.

Hugh Lupton

The Three Spinners

Origin
German.
Age range
Seven upwards.
Time
Twelve minutes.

This is a story collected by The Brothers Grimm. I first heard it in Germany, told by a woman while she was spinning. The sound of the spinning wheel going round and round was like a rhythmic drum beat accompanying her words. When she came to an important bit of the story she would stop spinning, and there was a magical silence.

Pomme Clayton

Mister Fox and his bag

Origin
English.
Age range
Five to seven years.
Time
Ten to fifteen minutes.

This story is found in both American and English folklore. Older children find the structure simple enough to be able to retell the tale to younger children.

There are also other stories found in Europe that feature a bag into which a dog is ultimately placed to see off the unpleasant owner – or stones are placed to fool the owner. The length of time this story takes to tell will depend on how much you wish to elaborate. Because of its structure, children from five years upwards find it very gripping. Afterwards they may wish to talk about what they liked and didn't like, draw their favourite part or draw a map of the story.

Pie Corbett

Piñoncita

Origin
Chilean.
Age range
Six to nine years.
Time
Fifteen minutes.

This was told to me by a woman from Chile. It has similarities with other stories from around the world, such as Tom Thumb, Thumbelina, etc. When I tell the story, I show the children a collection of objects which appear in the story. In the original story, the main character was a boy.

Mary Medlicott

Kakarat

Origin
Dominican.

This is the story of Kakarat who rescues his three vain and unkind sisters from the half man, half monster, Zokla.

Age range
Five to eleven years.
Time
Twelve to fifteen minutes.

Audience participation always works well with this one, with children playing the various animals who help Kakarat to rescue his sisters.

Jane Grell

The wooden trough

Origin
Russian.
Age range
Eight to eleven years.
Time
Ten minutes.

Originally told to me by my paternal grandfather, this story is traditional and there are various versions found throughout eastern Europe. The story shows the importance of treating your parents well. There is a version published by the brothers Grimm.

Pamela Marre

The black dog

Origin
Hebridean.
Age range
Seven to eleven years.
Time
Ten minutes.

One day when I was staying on the island of Iona, severe weather kept me indoors and I pulled a book from the shelf of the farmhouse in which I was staying. It was called *In the Highlands and Islands* by John McPhee. In it was a brief outline of the legend, and I fleshed out that outline in my own style.

Kelvin Hall

Little Semyon

Origin
Russian.
Age range
Four to seven years.
Time
Twelve minutes.

A shape-changing fairy tale, where everything gets repeated the magical three times.

Tim Bowley

The Old Witch

Origin
English.
Age range
Six to eight years.
Time
Ten minutes.

A fairy tale, with the motif of the selfish brother (or sister) getting his come-uppance. This is a common theme in stories across the world. 'Mother Holle' in Grimms' Fairy Tales is clearly a sister to this story.

Hugh Lupton

The seven ravens

Origin
German.
Age range
Six upwards.
Time
Ten minutes.

This fairy tale contains the motif of humans turning into birds. This is a common theme all over Europe. This version can be found in The Brothers Grimm collection. It was one of the fairytales I loved as a child.

Pomme Clayton

The White Bear King

Origin
Norwegian.
Age range
Seven upwards.
Time
Fifteen minutes.

This fairytale has parallels with the Greek myth of Cupid and Psyche. Other versions may be found from many other areas including Scotland and Russia. It has many female characters, including a determined heroine. The structure of the narrative is made up of repeating threes. It is fun to count them.

Pomme Clayton

Golden Star

Origin
German.
Age range
Seven upwards.
Time
Ten minutes.

In the Grimms' collection this story is known as 'The twelve brothers', which seems strange as it is really about Golden Star, so I've changed the title and one or two other things to make it right for me.

Tim Bowley

For dear life

Origin
English.
Age range
Nine upwards.
Time
Five minutes.

This story is a World War One myth.

Fred Sedgwick

The butterfly king

Origin
Original material.
Age range
Seven years.
Time
Twenty-five minutes.

This story really wrote itself one night, very soon after I became a storyteller.

Tim Bowley

Matiwara's name game

Origin
East African.
Age range
Five to seven years.
Time
Ten minutes.

I first heard this story from my grandfather when I was about seven years old. Grandfather was a very adventurous person. He was born in India. He sailed in an Arab dhow from India to East Africa to seek his fortune. He travelled around in the villages of Kenya, buying fruit from the villagers and selling it to shopkeepers in the small towns. He would be gone for days on his travels but when he returned, it was a very exciting time for everyone. He was full of stories about his travels and everybody would gather round the charcoal fire in the evening, to listen to his stories. 'Matiwara's name game' was one of the stories that he told us from one of his visits to a village near Lake Victoria.

Usha Bahl

The story with no ending

Origin
English.
Age range
Six to seven years.
Time
Ten minutes.

I found this story written as the title story in a collection of stories retold by Elizabeth Clark. The publication date was in the 1920s. I have also heard it on a number of occasions retold in various versions with locusts, bees and mice replacing the ants. There is a North Indian version by Nikhat Mohamed in Helen East's *Look Lively, Rest Easy* (A.&C.Black, 1990) in which it is birds that keep taking the grain. The story also relates to the family of stories about people who love or hate stories, and Helen East's collection includes such a story by Duncan Williamson.

What I like about telling this story is the eye-contact you have to use. The number of repetitions about the ants and the grains of corn depends on the audience's reaction. Keep a straight face and use a matter-of-fact tone of voice, and enjoy the gradual realisation of the joke first by individuals and then by everyone. Try it with different age-groups. Digressions on drought, famine, the behaviour of ants, etc. can help to distract the audience from keeping the point of the king's competition in mind.

Tony Aylwin

Penteclemas and the pea

Origin
Greek.
Age range
Eight to twelve years.
Time
Twenty minutes.

This is a story which I first came across, as a version by Ruth Manning Saunders. I performed it for many years in my South Bank concerts with the pianist Jean Phillips: the Gerard & Jean Concerts. We used piano music by Shostakovich to accompany it.

When I am telling this story, with or without music, I am

quite mobile. I indicate the dragon's size, for instance, by pacing about; and I incorporate features of the place I am in. Although the voices for the different characters should be differentiated, they should all be related to the storyteller's persona. The storyteller should be a bit like Penteclemas (naive and lovable) – and even the king should not be too posh: Penteclemas's idea of a king perhaps.

Gerard Benson

Two boys eating nuts

Origin
Gaelic.
Age range
Five to six years.
Time
Ten minutes.

A cumulative story from the Isle of Barra. I've tried to keep something of the music of the original Gaelic telling in the refrain of the story.

Hugh Lupton

Gawain and the loathly lady

Origin
British.
Age range
Nine upwards.
Time
Ten minutes.

This is one of those stories that all storytellers seem to know without being totally sure where they first heard it – certainly true for me anyway – so this is my version, from the many that I have heard and read of this great story.

Tim Bowley

A riddle-a-ring-a-roses

Origin
Arabic.
Age range
Nine to eleven years.
Time
Five minutes.

The beginning of this story (There was, there was not) is the traditional Arab way of starting a story. My version of this tale has evolved over many years of telling it to sophisticated teenagers, who start off sceptical and end up desperate to guess the ending. There is also a similar version by the Brothers Grimm.

Helen East

Washing-up water

Origin
Welsh.
Age range
Six to nine years.
Time
Ten minutes.

I like this story because it reminds me of the people in my grandparents' part of the country and their way of life. It is a traditional tale, but I have adapted the ending slightly to emphasise the importance of the leeks!

Mary Medlicott

The farmer and the unicorn

Origin
English.
Age range
Six to eleven years.
Time
Five minutes.

The first version of this story I heard was from Mike Rust, who runs the Tales from the Edge storytelling club in Shropshire and is very involved in encouraging storytelling nationwide. However, I have transposed the story in location, detail and wording.

Kelvin Hall

The stone

Origin
English.
Age range
Six to seven years.
Time
Five minutes.

This is a humorous tale with perhaps the modern equivalent being to use super-glue to stick a pound coin to the pavement and watch people trying to pull it off the ground.

Pie Corbett

Kanai's betel nut

Origin
Asian.

I once spent several months with a Brahmin family in the heart of rural Kerala. In the evenings, Naryanan, the father, lit

Age range
Four to seven years.
Time
Seven to ten minutes.

the lamp (there was no electricity), and we'd sit out on the porch, the cicadas chirruping madly in the background and the children clamouring for a story at our feet.

'Appoh…,' the old grandmother would lean back against the cool stone wall, and take her time before she began. Every so often she would stop narrating to ask for confirmation: sometimes the children burst out excitedly in reply, sometimes they just nodded and sighed. 'Appoh…,' she'd go on with the tale.

I've tried to put some of her into this Keralan story, but there is also quite a lot from all the children and adults with whom I have shared the story over the years.

It's a lovely story for leading into drama, dance and art work: one group came up with an elephant as big as their hall, another made a chain of villagers leading all round the school.

Helen East

The nixie of the pond

Origin
German.
Age range
Seven and upwards.
Time
Twelve minutes.

This little gem is gleaned from the Grimms' collection and seems, to me at least, to be a story of initiation into the Feminine.

Tim Bowley

The silver bell

Origin
Danish.
Age range
Seven to nine years.
Time
Six minutes.

This story was told to me by a Danish friend in response to me telling her 'The peddlar of Swaffham', a well known English version of the same tale. So one story often gets another. I think I've developed the characters of the brothers a bit, but really they are archetypes.

Helen East

Two furious red eyes

Origin
British.
Age range
Eight upwards.
Time
Eight minutes.

This modern tale was based on the traditional story of 'Slam and the Ghost', taken from Kevin Crossley-Holland's *British Folk Tales*.

Hugh Protherough

The apples of Iduna

Origin
Norse.
Age range
Seven upwards.
Time
Fifteen minutes.

This story comes from the early days of the gods and goddesses. The magical apples help them to stay young. The ending is very exciting and only a clever trick can save them.

Pie Corbett

Don't touch, Pandora

Origin
Greek.
Age range
Five upwards.
Time
Five minutes.

This is a story of temptation. I tell the story in different ways; either I mime the box or I bring in a special casket. Sometimes I get the children to mime a box for themselves. We lift up the lid and peer inside. Or I put my box down near the children in front and say, 'Now, whatever happens, don't look inside – don't even touch that box.' Of course, there is always someone who can't resist the temptation.

Pie Corbett

Baucis and Philemon

Origin
Greek.
Age range
Four to eleven years.
Time
Twenty to thirty minutes.

This Greek myth is one of the many Flood stories (although in my story I do not allow the people to drown; they flee instead). This version is from a period of work I did with a professional artist in an infant school in Redbridge.

Betty Rosen

The cyclops and the mermaid

Origin
Greek.
Age range
Seven upwards.
Time
Eight minutes.

I like telling this story because the children often feel sorry for the Cyclops, even though he gets angry with terrible consequences.

Pie Corbett

The spider's web

Origin
Greek.
Age range
Seven upwards.
Time
Ten minutes.

This is a good story to tell because the ending is very effective. I try not to give away what is going to happen.

Pie Corbett

The death of Baldur

Origin
Norse.
Age range
Seven upwards.
Time
Fifteen minutes.

This story brings to an end this final section of mythology. When I tell the story I can see poor Hodur beguiled into killing his own brother. The ending of the story is one of great hope.

Pie Corbett

Index of Titles

Index of Themes

Adam and Eve 16
Animals 10, 13, 16, 18, 30, 52, 66,
77, 83, 87, 90, 97, 99, 111, 123,
128, 137, 148, 150, 153, 161, 167
Ants 130
Archery 10

Battles 7, 48, 97, 99, 121, 142, 161
Bears 66, 111
Beauty 20, 33, 90, 118
Birds 7, 10, 13, 20, 75, 77, 87, 90,
108, 111, 118, 123, 132, 137, 150,
161, 167, 170, 174
Blacksmiths 90, 111
Brothers 23, 37, 52, 87, 90, 103,
108, 118, 156, 158, 174
Bullies 20, 26, 27, 66, 90

Castles 111, 118, 161
Cows 10, 23, 33, 41, 45, 52, 103,
137, 145
Creation 7, 9, 16

Daughters 20, 45, 68, 79, 90, 97,
108, 111, 118, 132, 158, 171, 174
Death 37, 41, 48, 57, 75, 97, 118,
130, 156, 161, 174
Disobedience 66, 87, 158, 165, 171
Dogs 16, 83, 90, 97, 118, 137, 174
Dragons 41, 132
Dreams 20, 123, 153, 156, 174

Earth 7, 9
Earthquakes 20

Families 20, 23, 37, 42, 52, 63, 68,
79, 87, 90, 94, 103, 108, 118, 121,
150, 153, 158
Farmers 27, 33, 52, 68, 71, 145,
148, 156
Fire 23, 26, 30, 33, 71, 77, 90, 118,
123, 161, 170, 174

Fish 11, 167
Fishermen 37, 167
Flying 13, 30, 118, 161, 165
Food 13, 41, 59, 63, 71
Frogs 77, 123, 158
Fruit 103, 161

Ghosts 158
Goddesses 161, 171
Gods, 7, 9, 16, 20, 57, 150, 161,
165, 167, 174
Gold 27, 103, 148, 156

Hags 111, 142, 174
Heaven 7, 23, 27, 150
Hunger 13, 16, 23, 30, 63, 71, 83,
87, 108, 111, 148, 150, 167

Jealousy 174
Journeys 42, 45, 52, 57, 71, 83, 99,
103, 108, 111, 123, 137, 142, 167

Kings 27, 33, 37, 48, 99, 111, 118,
123, 130, 132, 142, 171

Lakes 20, 137
Liars 23, 27, 30, 33
Little people 87, 145
Loyalty 90, 94, 97, 108, 111, 118,
153
Love 57, 59, 94, 99, 111, 118, 132,
144, 153, 167, 170, 174

Magic 59, 123, 153
Marriage 45, 57, 59, 79, 103, 111,
118, 130, 132, 142, 153, 161
Mermaids 170
Money 27, 33, 42, 52, 57, 71, 99,
118, 150, 153, 156
Moon 11, 18, 27, 39, 45, 90, 108,
153

Acknowledgements

**The publishers gratefully acknowledge permission to
reproduce the following copyright material:**

© 1993 Sandra A. Agard for 'The story of the Sun, the Moon and the Sea' and 'Tortoise and the party in the sky';
© 1993 Tony Aylwin for 'Soap' and 'The story with no ending'; © 1993 Usha Bahl for 'Matiwara's name game'; © Gerard Benson for 'The king who liked a good yarn' and 'Penteclemas and the pea';
© Leila Berg for 'Uncle Bouki's wow';
© 1993 Tim Bowley for 'Feathertoes', 'Golden Star', 'Ivan Berenekov', 'Sir Gawain and the loathly lady', 'The butterfly king', 'The nixie of the pond' and 'Little Semyon'; © Pomme Clayton for 'Master of all Masters', 'The man in search of his luck', 'The seven ravens', 'The Three Spinners' and 'The White Bear King'; © Pie Corbett for 'The apples of Iduna', 'Don't touch, Pandora', 'The cyclops and the mermaid', 'The spider's web', 'The death of Baldur', 'The king who lost his queen', 'Peapods', 'The lion and the foolish traveller', 'Mister Fox and his bag' and 'The stone';
© 1993 Mike Dunstan for 'Clever Mary and the stone soup'; © 1993 Helen East for 'A-riddle-a-ring-a-roses', 'The hazel stick', 'Kanai's betel nut' and 'The silver bell'; © 1993 Margaret Greaves for 'The dragon of Filey Brig'; © 1993 Jane Grell for 'Kakarat'; © 1993 Kelvin Hall 'The black dog', 'The farmer and the unicorn' and 'Pwyll and Rhiannon'; © 1993 Hugh Lupton for 'The three sillies', 'You're a liar!', 'Coyote the trickster', 'The Old Witch' and 'Two boys eating nuts';
© 1993 Pamela Marre for 'How music came to the world', 'The power of the small', 'The parrot's advice' and 'The wooden trough'; © 1993 Mary Medlicott for 'Piñoncita' and 'Washing-up water';
© 1993 Hugh Protherough for 'The farmer and the boggart' and 'Two furious red eyes'; © 1993 James Riordan for 'The Man in the Moon' and 'Bella and the bear'; © 1993 Betty Rosen for 'Baucis and Philemon'; © 1993 Fred Sedgwick for 'For dear life'; © 1993 Paula Sorhaindo for 'The pitch lake'; © 1993 Barrie Wade for 'Six suns (or how the cock got its comb)'; © 1993 Duncan and Linda Williamson for 'Archie's besom'.